D1452532

THEOLOGY AND SCIENCE AT THE FRONTIERS OF KNOWLEDGE

NUMBER SEVEN

SCIENCE AND THE GOSPEL

THEOLOGY AND SCIENCE AT THE FRONTIERS OF KNOWLEDGE

THEOLOGY AND SCIENCE AT THE FRONTIERS OF KNOWLEDGE

GENERAL EDITOR – T.F. TORRANCE

SCIENCE AND THE GOSPEL

VICTOR H. FIDDES

SCOTTISH ACADEMIC PRESS
EDINBURGH
1987

Published in association with the
Center of Theological Enquiry, Princeton
and
The Templeton Foundation
by
SCOTTISH ACADEMIC PRESS
33 Montgomery Street, Edinburgh EH7 5JX

First published 1987

ISBN 0 7073 0519 5

British Library Cataloguing in Publication Data

Fiddes, Victor H.
  Science and the Gospel.—(Theology
  and science at the frontiers of
  knowledge; 7)
  1. Religion and science—1946–
  I. Title   II. Series
  261.5'5   BL240.2

  ISBN 0–7073–0519–5

Printed in Great Britain by
H Charlesworth & Co Ltd

CONTENTS

To Norma

GENERAL FOREWORD

A vast shift in the perspective of human knowledge is taking place, as a unified view of the one created world presses for realisation in our understanding. The destructive dualisms and abstractions which have disintegrated form and fragmented culture are being replaced by unitary approaches to reality in which thought and experience are wedded together in every field of scientific inquiry and in every area of human life and culture. There now opens up a dynamic, open-structured universe, in which the human spirit is being liberated from its captivity in closed deterministic systems of cause and effect, and a correspondingly free and open-structured society is struggling to emerge.

The universe that is steadily being disclosed to our various sciences is found to be characterised throughout time and space by an ascending gradient of meaning in richer and higher forms of order. Instead of levels of existence and reality being explained reductionistically from below in materialistic and mechanistic terms, the lower levels are found to be explained in terms of higher, invisible, intangible levels of reality. In this perspective the divisive splits become healed, constructive syntheses emerge, being and doing become conjoined, an integration of form takes place in the sciences and the arts, the natural and the spiritual dimensions overlap, while knowledge of God and of his creation go hand in hand and bear constructively on one another.

We must now reckon with a revolutionary change in the generation of fundamental ideas. Today it is no longer philosophy but the physical and natural sciences which set the pace in human culture through their astonishing revelation of the rational structures that pervade and underly all created reality. At the same time, as our science presses its inquiries to the very boundaries of being, in macrophysical and microphysical dimensions alike, there is being brought to light a hidden traffic between theological and scientific ideas of the most far-reaching significance for both theology and science. It is in that situation where theology and science are found to have deep mutual relations, and increasingly cry out for each other, that our authors have been at work.

The different volumes in this series are intended to be geared into this fundamental change in the foundations of knowledge. They do not present "hack" accounts of scientific trends or theological fashions, but are intended to offer inter-disciplinary and creative interpretations which will themselves share in and carry forward the new synthesis transcending the gulf in popular understanding between faith and reason, religion and life, theology and science. Of special concern is the mutual modification and cross-fertilisation between natural and theological science, and the creative integration of all human thought and culture within the universe of space and time.

What is ultimately envisaged is a reconstruction of the very foundations of modern thought and culture, similar to that which took place in the early centuries of the Christian era, when the unitary outlook of Judaeo-Christian thought transformed that of the ancient world, and made possible the eventual rise of modern empirico-theoretic science. The various books in this series are written by scientists and by theologians, and by some who are both scientists and theologians. While they differ in training, outlook, religious persuasion, and nationality, they are all passionately committed to the struggle for a unified understanding of the one created universe and the healing of our split culture. Many difficult questions are explored and discussed, and the ground needs to be cleared of often deep-rooted misconceptions, but the results are designed to be presented without technical detail or complex argumentation, so that they can have their full measure of impact upon the contemporary world.

Science and the Gospel comes from the pen of one who has had a long and distinguished ministry in the United Church of Canada, for most of the time in Montreal. Throughout this ministry Dr Fiddes has brought to it a profound interest in the arts and sciences, in the belief that truth properly grasped and appreciated is everywhere found to be harmoniously linked in the universe that God has created and given to us as our home. This conviction bore fruit in earlier years in the publication of a book on architecture in which he sought to interrelate the arts and Christian worship. The present work emerged, as he tells us, "from the necessity of preaching", under an ever-growing conviction that the Gospel must be proclaimed and interpreted within the context of our scientific understanding of the created universe. The difficulty which he kept on meeting, however, and which made the preaching of the Gospel an almost impossible task, was the wide gap that had opened up in people's minds between the essence of the Christian faith in Christ and the scientific culture it had inspired. Hence in his regular preaching and teaching of the Gospel, Dr Fiddes showed that it is a serious mistake to assume that a properly scientific understanding of nature requires a repudiation of the biblical understanding of the world and a rejection of Christ as himself the way, the truth and the life. At the same time he set himself to work out for his congregations a deeper consideration of the relationship of natural science and Christian belief in which the deep wound in the prevailing outlook might be healed. He found that as a matter of fact a paradigmatic shift has been taking place in the conceptual structure of modern science in which the self-sufficiency of science itself is seriously challenged and the need for a deep-level integration between science and faith is found to be necessary if the new dimensions of reality being brought to light through scientific discovery are to be adequately grasped and relevantly integrated in our human life. *Science and the Gospel* is the fruit of that life-long ministry. It is written in a modest and yet challenging way which will undoubtedly be helpful to many people today.

We are very grateful to the Rev. Robert T. Walker of Edinburgh for generous help with the proofs.

Thomas F. Torrance

PREFACE

THE need for an introduction to this book is obviated by the content of chapter one, "Back to the Ivory Tower". The reader who finishes this first chapter will discover why the book has been written. I am aware, of course, that the attempt of a pastor to relate a subject as comprehensive and specialized as "science" to what he is bold enough to call the truth of the Gospel is to step into waters the undertow of which can quickly take him beyond his depth. The justification for undertaking this task is that necessity is laid upon me. I happen to believe, with Michael Green, that "It is high time for those who do not share reductionist Christology to stand up and be counted." Have not theologians themselves been insisting that we must all do theology? While I am not sure what this injunction means, I am convinced that one of the mandates of the preacher today is that he should try to bridge the gulf which separates the pew from the class-room, whether the class-room be in the theological school or the hall of science.

There remain the privilege and responsibility of paying tribute where tribute is due. Many people have made this book possible. Not least deserving of tribute are those patient and tolerant people of my congregations who, over a period of forty years, have ungrudgingly furnished that milieu for study and reflection, for reading and contemplation, without which basic convictions do not formalise. If we of the pastorate have not taken full advantage of this vocational opportunity whose fault is it?

I have dedicated this book to my wife Norma who has not only shared the most important years of my life but has shared those basic values of the Christian Faith which undergird home and family life. Thanks must also go to my brother, Dr Gladstone W. Fiddes of Edmonton, who, before a tragic illness, gave whole-hearted moral and material support to this enterprise. My thanks are also due to his daughters, Gladys and Margo, and to Dr Gordon Kramer, who busied themselves at the word processor on my behalf.

Obviously the content of a book like this must be exposed to specialists who are knowledgeable in the fields concerned. I am indebted to a number of scientists who, strangers at the time, were good enough to read and criticize carefully the text. This kind of criticism, needful as it is, can be intimidating to a layman, but had it not been for the sustained interest and encouragement of Professor T. F. Torrance of Edinburgh I doubt whether this book would have come to publication. Whatever qualifications this work may possess or lack there is no question in my mind that its intention, which is to explore science and theology at the frontiers of knowledge, is an urgent requirement of the time. To have a slot in the series devoted to this important task is a privilege and an honor.

5841 Bellevue Terrace,   Victor Fiddes
Niagara Falls,
Ontario, L2G 4G4

CHAPTER I

BACK TO THE IVORY TOWER

RECENT developments in natural science, particularly in physics, cosmology and biology have created an openness on the part of the scientific community to the possibility of renewed dialogue with religion. In society itself a growing anxiety concerning the human enterprise challenges science and religion to bring a common understanding to bear upon the question of the meaning of life and the nature of its ultimate realities.

The irony in the situation is that the leadership of the Christian churches which, for two centuries, has been deploring the existence of the gulf between science and religion now shows, for the most part, only a casual interest in the significance of these developments. It is engaged elsewhere.

Professor Robert Jastrow of NASA's Goddard Institute for Space Studies brings his book *God and the Astronomers* to a dramatic close with the observation that

> for the scientist who has lived by his faith in the power of reason, the story ends like a bad dream. He has scaled the mountains of ignorance. He is about to conquer the highest peak; as he pulls himself over the final rock he is greeted by a band of theologians who have been sitting there for centuries.[1]

Unfortunately the present band of Protestant theologians is not likely to be found in that exalted company of intellectuals who contemplate the mysteries of the universe from an Olympian height. With a few notable exceptions they are more likely to be found down on the plains of human endeavour where they are "doing theology" in areas of political awareness and social concern. I say "unfortunately" because, worthy as the

motives for involvement may be, the dimensions of the
Gospel are larger than those required for the building of a
better world. They have to do with the understanding and
transformation of human life and being which result from
the believers' being in Christ. The Christian message
ultimately stands or falls on the truth claim that "God was
in Christ reconciling the world to *himself*".

An illustration of this failure of the leadership of the
churches to be at the place where its credibility is staked is
provided by the agenda which was fixed for the
conference called by the World Council of Churches at
Cambridge, Massachusetts, in the summer of 1979 to
consider "Faith, Science and the Future". The conference brought together nine hundred people from fifty-six
nations who were specialists in various areas of science,
technology and religion. One might have assumed that in
the discussions of an assembly thus informed priority
would have been given to the task of framing dialogue for
the better understanding of science and the Christian
faith; and it is true that one particular area of study,
"Faith, Science and Human Understanding", did concern itself with the relationship of faith to the expanding
frontiers of natural science. It soon became apparent,
however, that the leadership of the conference was not so
much interested in the relationship of science to faith or of
faith to science as in the "struggle for a just, participatory
and sustainable society", and the conference ended by
issuing the usual political and economic pronouncements
which have characterized the work of that body in recent
years.

This pragmatism on the part of Christian leadership,
this need to be worldly-wise, traces back to a loss of nerve
consequent upon the dethronement of theology from its
time-honoured role as queen of the sciences. For the
better part of a century now the intellectual community
has been dominated by a structuralist or positivist point
of view which renders a theological understanding of life
irrelevant. Of this philosophy I shall have more to say in
the next chapter where I consider the parameters of

science. In passing let me say that the assumption underlying this view is that man is adequately equipped within
himself to master human life and destiny and that if
meaning is to be found in life and the world it will be
found in the achievement of a "human good" apart from
metaphysical principles. Knowledge of truth thus becomes synonymous with discoveries which are made
experimentally by the human intellect. Since all areas of
knowledge have now been subjected to this critique
concepts of a metaphysical kind which cannot thus be
rationalized are simply ignored. Jacques Ellul has said
that "To the degree, in fact, to which objectivity stems
from pure methodology, then becomes a state of consciousness, an attitude, an ethic it becomes a value
judgement, an exclusion of every other mode of apprehending truth."[2] Religious truth itself has not escaped the
judgement of this kind of objectivity. Richard Quebedeaux writes: "The rational methodology inherent in
modernity requires that social phenomena of all kinds,
including religion, be interpreted less and less in moral
and theological terms and more and more by reference to
empirical evidence about society itself."[3]

Nothing succeeds like success, and the spectacular
technological achievements of the nineteenth and the
twentieth centuries have so bolstered man's self-confi-
dence as to render him incapable of coming to the
understanding of reality in any way other than through
observation and experiment. Of this fact the modern
theologian is poignantly aware. He experiences vocation-
ally the truth of Heinrich Heine's observation made over
a century ago: "Die Wohungsnot hat für Gott angetre-
ten". ("The housing problem has arisen for God!")

In recent years, however, a remarkable thing has
happened, and it has happened in the very circles which
hitherto have been most closely allied with the structuralist's point of view and have given it its most prestigious
support. I refer to the unease which exists in the circle of
scholars who work in the most sophisticated areas of
natural science — physics, cosmology and biology in

particular — an unease which is now filtering down to other areas and is bound eventually to affect the orientation of natural science.

The unease of which I speak is not to be confused with the practical frustration which is everywhere felt today with regard to the material developments which are a byproduct of natural science. Everyone knows that there has been a souring in the material realm and that science isn't delivering just the kind of goodies that were expected from its cart. Recognition of this fact, however, has not led to a general awareness that there is anything basically wrong with the structuralist system. Indeed, the more rapidly the human situation deteriorates the stronger man's reliance upon his technological resourcefulness seems to be. The ubiquitous plea in this decade of the eighties — a decade which is witnessing the collapse of virtually all systems, structures and theories — is the frenzied plea for more adequate planning and research. God help the nation that fails to give priority to Research and Development so that the latest software of its computerized society can be available to every child who leaves the nursery!

The unease to which I refer is the growing recognition on the part of people who are closest to theoretical science that things in the material realm are not what they appear to be, that man does not really have the answers and, apart from the illumination of faith, is not likely to get them. I am aware that this may not be the impression gained from looking at science TV or reading current popular science. The general impression is that natural science is now on the verge of solving the riddle of the universe and that if it is just given a little more time and a lot more money this goal will be attained. More realistic, it seems to me, is the conclusion of Professor T. F. Torrance: "Natural science through its remarkable intelligibility cries out for a proper doctrine of creation."[4]

It seems to me that when a 'Macedonian' call like this is heard the leadership of the Church should not be so engaged with the material problems of the world that it cannot respond. It should have some of its most powerful reserves in the ivory tower.

Let me now enlarge upon what I perceive to be the openness of the situation and the nature of the Macedonian call which is coming to the community of faith.

Professor Walter R. Thorson of Edmonton recently made the following observation:

> When I began to think about philosophical problems, or even to cope with general ideas about scientific work, it became very evident to me that certain recurrent themes and ideas which in scripture have their immediate application to fundamental spiritual issues, also have a "mirroring" or congruent relevance in relation to questions and problems encountered in man's relation to reality at lesser levels. This is because many of these principles or ideas focus on epistemological issues, that is, the nature of real knowing and its functional manifestations.[5]

I am sure that many of us who do not possess Professor Thorson's scientific qualifications have felt this way. We have heard remarkable and puzzling things about the new knowledge which science furnishes of the elementary particle. We have been told that physical matter itself is not the tangible "thing" it appears to be, and that at its elemental level it fails even to "exist" in the accepted sense of that word. We are informed that quantum mechanics implies an unpredictability in particle behaviour, the mathematical description of which sounds suspiciously noetic. We learn that Newtonian measurements fail to relate to physical reality both at the subatomic level and in its cosmic dimensions. We have been fascinated to learn about the supremacy of light in the universe and its dominance in the field of energy. We discover that time, which no one seems quite able to define, is an essential corollary of space. Turning from physics to biology we marvel at the way the DNA molecule carries the "word", and we find respectable company sharing the suspicion that a doctrinaire theory of natural selection fails to answer some important questions concerning the origin of life and the development of living forms. In cosmology we learn that the "singularity" in the act of creation confounds basic laws of physics which we assumed were universal, and implies an insoluble mystery at pre-Planck time.

Some of us who are believing Christians cannot help but notice a remarkable affinity between these interests of twentieth century science and the thrust of the biblical revelation, and we find our conviction strengthened that modern science, while needing the full scope of free enquiry, might profitably benefit from the metaphysical support which this revelation provides.

Robert A. Herrmann, Assistant Professor of Mathematics at the U.S. Naval Academy, writing in the *Journal of the American Scientific Affiliation*, said:

> There exists a considerable amount of personal, experiential, behaviouristic, historical, linguistic, statistical, and purely scientific evidence which may empirically establish that the major concepts of Christianity are true. One of my major concerns is why the scientific, political and philosophical communities as well as millions of ordinary everyday individuals, do not accept the evidence.[6]

I suppose the reason science continues to treat with a certain suspicion the encroachment of the theologian on its territory is because of the Church's historic blunders in this field. We are told that the Church has periodically resisted the work of natural science and has rewarded some of its most significant discoveries with witch hunt and persecution. To this day scarcely a week passes in the year without another reference to the Church's condemnation of Galilei Galileo, the reminder being that science then stood on the side of truth and integrity whereas a reactionary Church defended falsehood and obscurity.[7]

It is probably futile to suggest that this is not quite the way things were four hundred years ago; efforts to straighten the record seem to be in vain. The Galileo debate, at least at the outset, was not a controversy between science and religion. It was a controversy among co-religionists (Copernicus himself was serving as a canon

at the Cathedral of Frauenburg while he compiled his
massive work on the movements of the planets and stars).
The Church at that time was the custodian of science and
was no more eager to leap to scientific conclusions than
the custodians of science are today. Some stood on one
side of the issue and some on the other. (Remember that
in this 20th century it has taken scientists sixty years to
come to terms with quantum mechanics, and that without
the delaying tactics of theologians!). E. A. Burtt in his
book, *The Metaphysical Foundations of Modern Science*,
has said that "contemporary empiricists, had they lived in
the 16th century, would have been the first to scoff out of
court the new philosophy of the universe".[8] What
happened was that a very important moral and philosophical consideration polarized around disputed astronomical
conjectures. As it turned out the opponents of Galileo
were dead wrong on their facts. But were they wrong in
clinging to their philosophy of science? The basic
question at issue was "Do man and his world have a
central place in the universe?" Is it not ironic that this
question has come back to haunt modern science, and that
on this issue the jury may have to be sent out again?

This sixteenth century controversy, so often presented
as an unhappy illustration of the danger of theology
meddling with science, might equally well provide a
classic illustration of the need for ongoing dialogue.
Truth is not something to be equated simply with factual
knowledge. Truth also involves moral insight and spiritual perception. Pascal said: "Knowledge of physical
science will not console me for ignorance of morality in
time of affliction, but knowledge of morality will always
console me for ignorance of physical science."[9]

I have not taken this philosophical detour to defend
religious obscurantism. Unfair as the judgment of history
on the Church may be, the fact remains that organized
religion carries a heavy burden of guilt from its reluctance
to embrace scientific discoveries made out of season, and
the burden of proof that the Church has mended its ways
still rests with the institution. Unfortunately obscuran-

tism is still to be found within its ranks and when, in our day, a wilful conservatism joins forces with pseudo-science to defend a literalistic interpretation of scriptural insights the results can only be detrimental to science and religion alike.

But there is a further difficulty in communication. Any person who is venturesome enough to engage in interdisciplinary work these days is likely to be tagged a dilletante by his colleagues. Scientific knowledge has become so specialized that the more a person knows of a particular field the more he isolates himself from specialists elsewhere. The sheer scale and the superorganized character of scientific research has proved something of a curse; while it assures getting detailed knowledge it discourages broader relationships of knowledge and militates against the gaining of wisdom. Alexander Solzhenitsyn speaks of "the increasingly narrow specialization of professional disciplines, which enables semi-ignoramuses to become doctors of science".[10]

Fortunately there are scholars who are knowledgable in both science and theology and possess the qualifications needed to spearhead the needed rapprochement. I think particularly of T. F. Torrance of Edinburgh whose contribution in this area has been outstanding and has gained for him the enviable Templeton award. There are other "few with vision" who command high respect in both scientific and religious communities. The very fact that these people are knowledgeable, however, means that their language tends to be academic, and their word does not readily filter down to the man on the street or the person in the pew. Perhaps the solution to the problem of communication is for the layperson to do it himself. By layperson I mean the man or the woman who is generally informed in science and respectful of its findings. But he does not allow the fact that he is not an expert to intimidate him, and he reserves the right to draw his own conclusions from the acknowledged facts.

As writer of the pages that follow I make no pretense to possess specialized knowledge of either science or of theology. I am a minister of the United Church of Canada who for more than forty years has tried to keep abreast of developments in natural science and of trends in Christian theology. Neither of these attempts has been easy, but the excitement of the former has compensated for the frustration of the latter. What I have tried to do in these pages is to present in an understandable yet not superficial way some of the remarkable things that natural science has brought to light in this century — a century which is coming to be known as the post-classical period of science — and to suggest the manner in which the Christian revelation brings its timeless light to bear on these developments.

The conclusion which I have reached, and which I would share with you is that the queen of the sciences, as Christian theology used to be called, might profitably reassert her place over the subordinate disciplines. I am under no illusion that the scientific community itself is prepared to greet such a proposal with universal enthusiasm, but I should like to think that this conclusion is reached, not simply from wishful thinking on my part, but from the realities of the situation which confronts the serious Christian who seeks understanding at the present stage of intellectual ferment.

NOTES

1. Robert Jastrow, *God and the Astronomers*, (W. W. Norton, New York, 1978), p. 116.
2. Jacques Ellul, *The New Demons*, (Seabury, New York, 1973), p. 60.
3. Richard Quebedeaux, *By What Authority?*, (Harper and Row, New York.), p. 26.
4. Thomas F. Torrance, *Christian Theology and Scientific Culture*, (Christian Journals, Belfast, 1980), p. 38.
5. "Origins and Change", *JASA*, Vol. 33, No. 33, 1981, p. 131.
6. "Origins and Change", *JASA*, 1978, p. 33.
7. Typical of this attitude is an article, *The Incredible Universe*, by Kenneth Weaver, which appeared in the May 1974 issue of *National Geographic Magazine*, p. 629. Accompanying the article was an artist's colourful rendering of Galileo pleading his case in the presence of cardinals of the Church. Galileo is depicted,

valiant for truth, with the integrity of the open-minded scientist whereas the ecclesiastic to whom he is showing the evidence has a rather vacuous countenance which displays scorn and contempt. This identification of the ecclesiastic with naivety and the scientist with realism is hardly fair. It is salutory to recall that the Vatican's Pontifical Academy of Science, of which Galileo himself was a progenitor, today lists twenty-two of its current seventy members as Nobel prize winners!

8. E. A. Burtt, *The Metaphysical Foundations of Modern Science*, p. 25. See also the article, "The Establishment of a Heliocentric Universe", by Jerry Bergman in *JASA*, vol. 33, no.4, p. 225.

9. Blaise Pascal, *Pensées*, II, 23.

10. Alexander Solzhenitsyn, *From Under the Rubble*, (Little, Brown and Company), Boston/Toronto, p. 254.

CHAPTER 2

THE PARAMETERS OF SCIENCE

BEFORE considering the possibility of relationships between science and the Christian faith it might be well to look at the frame of reference within which modern science has been operating, and to consider the underlying principles which, up to the present time, have determined the scope of its operation and fixed the form of its expression. And if, in the pages which immediately follow, I seem to be blurring the prospect which I have just heralded of a better day for science and religion, it is because the new stage setting seems to require a refocusing of the lights.

Historically close relations have existed between science and religion with religion traditionally influencing if not framing the concepts of science. According to the thinking of many serious people it was Christianity itself which made possible the development of modern science in its present form. Interesting in this regard is an observation of the late J. W. N. Sullivan in his book *The Limitations of Science*:

> Although the scholastic outlook discouraged scientific inquiry, it furnished an essential element of the scientific outlook itself. This was the belief in nature as a rational whole. In the medievalist's universe, unlike that of the Babylonians and other early peoples, nothing was capricious or arbitrary. This belief, that "every detailed occurrence can be correlated with its antecedents in a perfectly definite manner, exemplifying general principles" is, as Whitehead says, the necessary basis for the whole scientific adventure. "Without this belief the incredible labours of scientists would be without hope." Yet this belief in universal order does not impose itself as a result of direct experience, as the very different conceptions prevalent in earlier times are sufficient to show. It may

even be that this belief will ultimately prove to be unjustified. It may be, as Eddington has hinted, that the universe will turn out to be finally irrational. This does not mean, of course, that the scientific knowledge so far obtained would be abandoned. As a set of working rules science would still be valid, for phenomena would presumably continue to occur in the same fashion as at present. But science would have reached a limit beyond which it could not go.

The development of science up to now, then, has assumed that nature is a rational whole, and this belief we owe, as a matter of history, to the great scholastic philosophers. Although therefore they achieved nothing, or practically nothing, in actual scientific discovery, they had a great deal to do with the formation of the modern scientific outlook.[1]

It is difficult to imagine how either the physical sciences or the social sciences could have come to anything like their present expression outside this framework of Hebrew-Christian thought. In view of this historic influence it seems somewhat ironic that the general attitude of science today is that it should isolate itself from Christian faith and experience. By way of explaining how this situation has come about let me contrast the intellectual outlook which prevailed at the beginning of the modern scientific era with that which prevails today.

As an illustration of the way things used to be let me recall the theory of orders which Blaise Pascal, the great French mathematician and physicist of the seventeenth century, employed in his literary fragment, *Les Pensées*. Pascal's concept of orders stemmed from a simple mathematical observation which he extended to embrace the whole conceptual realm. Pascal remarked that lines, squares and cubes (x, x^2 and x^3) cannot be added together; they each stand in their own right and belong to different orders. A single straight line can never incorporate a square, but a square can and does incorporate straight lines; a square can never embrace a cube, but a cube can and does embrace squares. Pascal conceived of life's entities as belonging to hierarchic orders which derive significance from their relationships. The lower is made meaningful through its incorporation into the higher. He described these orders variously as flesh, mind, will; knowledge, reason, heart (love or charity); body, mind, spirit; summarily, "things, man and God". Under "things" would be subsumed such entities as money, technology and science which derive their significance from the uses to which man puts them. Thus the famous saying of Article 308 of his *Pensées*:

> All bodies, the firmament, the stars, the earth, and its kingdoms are not worth the least of minds, for it knows them all and itself too, while bodies know nothing.
>
> All bodies together and all minds together and all their products are not worth the least impulse of charity. This is of an infinitely superior order.
>
> Out of all bodies together we could not succeed in creating one little thought. It is impossible, and of a different order. Out of all bodies and minds we could not extract one impulse of true charity. It is impossible, and of a different, supernatural order.

Pascal added that it is through the heart that man knows first principles, and it is on such knowledge, "coming from the heart and instinct" (Art. 110), that reason depends and bases all its principles.

I have cited Pascal here because his use of orders illustrates the kind of conceptual thinking to which both science and religion could relate in the early period of modern classical science. For two centuries this theory of orders furnished a helpful paradigm for Christians and others who wanted to find a secure place in their understanding for both factual knowledge and religious faith. Even today many of us would like to think that the material things of life, including the data and the constructs which natural science employs, belong to an order of things which stands under man and serves in his employ. The telescope through which an Edwin Hubble is looking sees nothing; the mathematical constructs he uses are not self-conceived. Science possesses nothing that it has not been given by man; it can be kept in its place, as it were.

The picture has changed radically, however, since the seventeenth century, and the relationship of man to things which then seemed neat and logical is no longer simple. Things now refuse to stand in the subservient role which that earlier age assigned them. On the contrary they have assumed an autonomy which increasingly puts man in their service.

Especially is this true of the things of science. Man no longer has a clean handle on science. A mystique of such magnitude now attaches to this enterprise that most people are prepared to grant it an autonomy which enables it to work independently of its human creator. The very person who insists that Hubble's telescope sees nothing would agree that when he is looking through it he must not be distracted by a nervous Christian peering over his shoulder wondering what "it" will discover. It seems to me that any consideration of the relationships that are possible between science and faith must take into account this conceptual shift in thinking, and give thought to the rationale which underlies the modern acceptance of the autonomy of natural science. Man no longer looks at things the way he used to. Modern man, Christian or otherwise, brings to science presuppositions which are alien to Pascal's understanding of ordered values.

In the preceding chapter I referred to the presuppositions of structuralist or positivist thought which have supplanted Christian thinking to become the dominant intellectual force of the times. Classical expression of this philosophy is found in Auguste Comte's *Cours de Philosophie Positive* (1830–1842) in which Comte, analysing the relation of social evolution and the stages of science, held that the method of rational investigation applied to material relationships furnishes the only legitimate means of understanding the nature of reality, physical or otherwise. The discovery by inductive method of the laws or sequences of phenomena, including the phenomenon of man himself, provides data which are "scientific", in contrast to speculative thought which is subjective and unprovable. According to this standpoint the quantities of science are solely those which are directly measurable or which have a capability of measurement, and the role of science is to reconcile the results of measurement without postulating an underlying reality to which it relates. As I shall point out in chapter IV this is not the way pure science comes to its most important discoveries, but this is the assumption under which modern science has done its experimental work. The French writer Gilbert Simondon speaks of this structuralist development as "a process conditioning the birth of a milieu instead of being conditioned by an already existing milieu".[2]

Thus was the way opened for science to become an autonomous enterprise which, like technology to which it can so easily relate, "ultimately depends only on itself, it maps its own route, it is a prime and not a secondary factor, it must be regarded as an 'organism' tending toward closure and self-determination".[3] Walter Thorson writes: "Having finally understood that scientific truth is a source of power, man has made the crucial decision that from now on the will to power and the uses of power should dictate the *relevance and value* (italics mine) of that truth."[4]

The remarkable thing here is the ease with which intellectuals in the "Christian" west adapted to this conceptual shift and gradually adjusted their faith to it. The situation was somewhat different in the country which officially embraced this positivist philosophy in its "scientific" materialism. Many of Russia's most perceptive intellectuals — men of the stature of Gogol, Tolstoi, Dostoievski, Soloviev, Fedorov and Berdyaev — refused to embrace a positivist philosophy because they felt that it could not be reconciled with the truth of the Christian faith. In our time Alexander Solzhenitsyn stands in this tradition of revolt, and the reaction of American intellectuals to his Harvard address in 1978 illustrates the gulf which separates these points of view. Modern man "values" things that work, and experimental science certainly works.

As natural science increasingly demonstrated the

practical advantage of technique over speculation the experimental method extended itself into areas of thought and influence which hitherto had been dominated by more metaphysical considerations. Hegel the German philosopher and educator said that "the hightest point in the development of a people is reached when they have reduced its laws, its ideas of justice and morality, to a science." Jacques Ellul maintains that once pure science gave priority to technical means this development had to transpire. Defining technique as "the totality of methods rationally arrived at and having absolute efficiency in every realm of human activity", he concludes that there is no way for science to free itself from the domination of technology.

Whether Ellul is right or wrong concerning the necessity of this development — the argument of this book rests on the hope that he can be wrong! — it is hard to challenge his assessment of the trend. In this century the scientific method has extended itself to embrace every realm of human enterprise, and concepts which cannot readily be accommodated to its analysis are largely ignored. As I write this chapter I have before me a press clipping which reports that a leading geneticist in the United States is urging the formation of a bank of human embryos to be used for research. His argument is that while the attempt to correct genetic defects in humans appears to be well beyond the line of what is presently possible such a development is inevitable in the future; hence the "urgent need" for research right now. The research, of course, would be done under ethical restraints with a watchdog committee of "doctors and others" monitoring the experiments. Suppose that among the others sitting on the committee a moral theologian (not a likely supposition!) were to propose that in the manipulation of genes primary consideration be given to those moral and spiritual qualities — gentleness, meekness, patience, a longing for truth, a thirst for righteousness — which attach to citizenship in the kingdom of heaven, would he not be reminded that such inward or spiritual qualities cannot be measured genetically and are therefore outside the field of scientific research?

In the nexus of modern thought the question of the relationship of natural science to Christian faith or, indeed, to any supposed higher level of understanding becomes somewhat academic. Where are these other levels found? In the soul? But what and where is the soul? If such levels were discovered, to what would they relate? To moral considerations? But are not moral considerations fixed by pragmatic needs? The dilemma of modern of science lies right here. Science finds itself unable to relate to metaphysical aspects of reality and yet its mandate requires that it command the approach to every field of knowledge. No flaming sword discourages the scientist from entering that part of the garden "east of Eden" where the fruit of the tree of life hangs ripe for the plucking. Alan Guth, a brilliant young physicist who has made a significant contribution to the study of cosmic origins, recently remarked: "In the sixties the big deal was in trying to calculate, say, cross sections for proton scattering at 5GeV. Now our goals are tremendously more ambitious. We want to be able to explain everything."[5]

The parameters of modern science are obviously very different from those of Blaise Pascal's day. As far as the understanding of the phenomenal world is concerned — and for natural science that is the only world that can matter — the order of significance is that which is perceived through logical analysis and arithmetical means. Since the knowable world provides ample and rewarding scope for this kind of knowledge science has succeeded in collecting and relating and partly apprehending a colossal amount of factual and theoretic knowledge. Mathematics in particular has proved spectacularly successful in uncovering aspects of physical reality which, apart from its competence, would have remained quite unknowable. J. C. Polkinghorne states, "Discovery is the name of the game. The pay-off for the rigours and *longueurs* of scientific research is the consequent gain in understanding the way the world is constructed."[6]

But the reality of life embraces more than factual and theoretic knowledge. The most significant aspects of reality are those which natural science, because of the abstract nature of its study has been forced to ignore. I refer to the moral and spiritual dimensions of life which relate to the being of man. The energy of love, for example, is certainly as "real" an energy as the energy of light; but the description of love does not mesh with the mathematics which science employs, and science has had to ignore its reality. A physical black hole, the existence of which is bound to remain somewhat conjectural, presents itself to science as a challenging "object" of study, whereas the fact of evil, the reality of which has been indubitably established in human experience, simply confounds physics.

The reminder that such metaphysical realities are incommensurate with the realities which natural science apprehends simply underlines the limitation of natural science. Science cannot have it both ways. It cannot "want to be able to explain everything" as long as it is forced by its presuppositions to ignore the most meaningful aspects of reality. Nor can it claim autonomy for its work unless it divides the field of understanding into two parts — that material or phenomenal part with which it is competent to deal, and that spiritual or noumenal (but no less phenomenal!) part to which it makes no attempt to relate. But if science assumes such a dualism what happens to its alleged goal, which is to find a basic unity in nature? By what logic does science exclude from nature its most significant aspect — the inner being of man?

Let us pause to consider the point that this limitation of natural science would not be of such serious consequence were it not for the fact that modern man is now almost entirely dependent upon its instruments for his conceptual understanding. Modern man, trained to think "scientifically" seems unable to make any kind of value judgement apart from a consideration that has to do with the control of the material world. A sobering illustration of this fact is the remark which President Nixon made in July, 1969 with reference to Neil Armstrong's spectacular landing on the moon: "This is the greatest week in the history of the world since the creation." After making due allowance for political hype the fact that a president could say such a thing without causing evident embarrassment to the intellectual community (Billy Graham did register a mild protest!) forces one to ask what criterion of values places the ability of an astronaut to step out of a tin can and take a walk on the moon ahead of the achievement of a Bach Fugue or a soliloquy of Shakespeare's Hamlet? Comic-strip artist Johnny Hart recently sketched his neanderthal character "B.C." peering into "Wiley's Dictionary" where he found Trivia Pursuit defined as "man's never-ending search for a lack of meaning". Man is still thus engaged, natural science itself providing classic illustration of an enterprise that has gained the whole world and lost its soul.

I am perfectly aware, of course, that, in reality, the scientist does not and cannot live by bread alone. The scientist is a human being before he becomes a scientist and he remains one afterwards. He knows that there has to be "good" reason for doing what he is doing or there would be no point in his doing it. Like Eve in the Genesis saga he perceives that the Tree of Life is "good" for food, that it is "pleasant" for the eyes, and a tree to be "desired" to make one "wise". So he invests his enterprise with meaning. This investment of moral worth in science explains why it seems entirely appropriate that the figure of Albert Einstein should be carved in stone above the Riverside Church in New York, whereas it would be unthinkable to have it placed above the Memorial to the Dead at Hiroshima! But it should be realized that this investment of moral worth and meaning in science is made possible only by removing the logic from logical positivism.

It seems to me that the inability of positivism even to face, much less come to grips with, this moral dilemma which it creates, has serious implications for a science which continues to rest upon its assumptions. Modern science cannot be challenged at the level of its technical competence; nor should its right to investigate every area which is open to this competence be questioned. Modern science can be challenged for its failure to relate to the realities of life which give the whole enterprise its rationale.

If natural science is going to work in a meaningful and responsible way, will it not have to break out of the closed system which thus circumscribes it? Why do these dimensions of material reality with which science has dealt so successfully appear to be incommensurate with the metaphysical realities which have motivated its work? Is it, as the Greeks assumed, because of some basic dualism in nature? Is it because a dichotomy exists between being and doing? Or is it because of the dictates of a philosophical premise which rules out relationship? D. Gareth Jones has said:

> It would be easy to see this distinction between closed and open systems as a distinction between scientific and non-scientific approaches, but this would be very misleading. Although a scientific approach may lend itself to a closed system, it does not predicate it. Moreover an open system has within it considerable scope for scientific investigation. At base, the differences between the two systems are philosophically determined, the characteristics of the system being derived from the initial premises.[6]

Let me try an analogy here. Sixty years ago it seemed that there was no way for physics to reconcile the wave and particle behaviour of the electron. The qualities were of quite different sorts. But in 1928 Paul Dirac solved the dilemma with his quantum field theory. The principle of superposition with its provision of vector spaces provided a sophisticated formula which added seemingly incompatible qualities together. We are told that for those in the know this formalism combines waves and particles without a trace of paradox. Using such an analogy might I ask whether in the epistemological scheme of things a kind of "superposition" is possible which would enable physics and metaphysics, or, science and faith, to correspond? If this is not possible then it seems to me that natural science is in continuing trouble. If it remains a bootstrap operation will it not reach Sullivan's "limit beyond which it could not go"? Some scientists fear that their enterprise may now have reached that limit. Natural science seems no longer able to communicate anything except the kind of information that relates to techniques of the material world, and that in symbols that are accessible only to specialists.

It is interesting that the Bible assumes no basic dualism in nature, and I rather suspect that in the ultimate reaches of the universe there will be discovered no separate Department of Physics, nor, for that matter a separate Chair of Systematic Theology? But even in this world where mortals peer and probe is it a foregone conclusion that no interface of physics with metaphysics is possible? Cosmologist Sir Fred Hoyle has recently written something which, maverick though he may be, deserves a hearing:

> People who devote a lifetime to a particular area often come to believe that the subject is their own personal property...But of course the Universe knows no such proprietary rights. Nor does the Universe know anything of the separation we make between biology and the other sciences — physics, astronomy and chemistry for example. All subjects in the world (underlining mine) must therefore be taken together, if we are to understand properly the way things are, and ideas have a relevance for themselves irrespective of the so-called branch of science they may come from.[8]

I underlined the words all subjects in the world because I think it is important to ask whether the moral and spiritual dimensions of life which, to my way of thinking, constitute the most significant aspects of reality, are to be exempted from Hoyle's requirement.

The kind of abstraction which has characterized the work of modern science may have had legitimacy in the eighteenth century when science had clear concepts of what it was observing and a clear understanding of the way its observed objects were behaving. As we have seen, there was in that earlier time of classical science an appropriate place slotted for God and man and things with open and workable relationships existing between the parts. But the situation is different today. Science may be asking the questions it asked in Newton's day: "Why are the laws of nature what they are?", "Why does the universe consist of the things it does?", but these questions are set in a different frame. WE are no longer in the time of classical science.

Let me sharpen the focus here by recalling a familiar statement of one who may be described as the greatest and the last in the line of the classical scientists: "The belief in an external world independent of the perceiving subject is the basis of all the natural sciences." I quote Albert Einstein here not because this particular statement adequately expresses the philosophy of science held by this remarkable man. (I shall have more to say about Einstein's philosophy in chapter IV.) His position actually was far removed from the positivism which I have just reviewed. I use this familiar quote because it expresses in a succinct way the basic scientific assumption of the eighteenth and nineteenth centuries: The investigator must separate himself from the world he would understand. The issue which I raise here is not the objective reality of that world. The issue is that of impingement. Can or should the perceiving subject oppose himself to that which he would understand? Science today is not so sure that this is the case.

If it were to become evident that it is impossible for the perceiving subject to quite separate himself from the world he is investigating would that mean that no basis remains for natural science? Might it not rather mean that natural science has to find a foundation broad enough and strong enough to support both man and nature interrelatedly? If this were to prove to be the case a subtle rewording of the scientific task would be required. Instead of asking, "What is the nature of that objective reality which man can know?", the question would be:

"What is the nature of the ultimate reality to which man is called to relate?."

Nicholas Berdyaev in his profound and penetrating analysis of history remarked that

> Between man and history there exists such a deep, mysterious, primordial and coherent relationship, such a concrete interdependence that a divorce between them is impossible. It is as impossible to detach man from history and to consider him abstractly as it is to detach history from man and to examine it from without, that is, from a non-human point of view.[9]

It should be realized that when Berdyaev spoke of the "historical" he did not mean what most people think of as history — a kind of continuum of external temporal events to be catalogued in linear sequence. He defined the historical as a *revelation of the deepest essence of universal reality, of the destiny of the world focused in man.*

Modern science in some of its studies (physics, chemistry, cosmology, for example) has completely ignored the subject of man — for what seemed an obvious reason — man was not its concern. In other studies (history, anthropology, sociology) science has had a great deal to say about man; but these studies, aspiring to be "scientific" in the accepted sense of the word, have treated man objectively and impersonally, an interesting and perhaps unique kind of referent, rather than as a focus of reality.

In view of this ingrained attitude of detachment it may be unrealistic now to expect natural science to initiate an enlargement of its parameters so as to embrace those metaphysical considerations which an understanding of the deepest essence of universal reality would seem to require. But if science in the course of its own investigations were to discover intimations of a reality which transcends its own established frame would not such intimations suggest the wisdom of a review of the parameters? This is what appears to be happening in various areas of natural science. As Walter Thorson has said:

According to positivist dogma, thinking about science would eventually scour away all the old metaphysical feelings we have about nature, but in fact modern physics and biology are increasingly full of philosophical questions that entail fantastic metaphysical loose ends, and scientists no longer ignore them as meaningless.[10]

One can appreciate the reluctance of modern science to entertain what William Pollard has called "rumors of transcendence".[11] Having rid his house of meddling theologians in the eighteenth and nineteenth centuries the scientist is naturally reluctant to welcome new and perhaps more terrible demons who are now seen coming down the epistemological trail to his place in growing numbers. Especially when these fellow travellers appear somewhat quarrelsome and incompatible in their own company! And yet if science is going to keep any kind of an open house it may have to suffer some of these fools gladly. Rumours often herald at least a partial truth, and it may be the responsibility of science as it moves into the vagaries of an uncertain future to "try the spirits to see whether they are of God".

My own bias here is already quite evident. Like the writer of the epistle just quoted I believe that the revelation of God in Jesus Christ stands apart from speculative and philosophical thought to provide specific data which are analogous to the needs of science. The conception here of a unique event both historical (open to natural science) and metaphysical (disclosed to faith) reveals the full dimensions of life and being, and relates itself to human understanding in a dynamic and meaningful way. In this distinctive revelation Eternity relates himself to space/time, the Infinite assumes a finite form, and Spirit and matter are conjoined. Being and doing are seen to be inseparable, means and ends indivisible, and the Medium (God in Christ) the message (reconciling the world to himself).

If human understanding were looking for a paradigm to embrace that ultimate unity of being which is the goal of conceptual thought it would be hard put to find a more adequate one than that which is provided in the disclosure of the Word made flesh. Is it unrealistic for the Christian who believes this way to urge natural science, along with every other endeavour of the human mind and spirit to consider the relevance to itself of the promise of him in whom the fullness of the Godhead dwells: "Hitherto ye have asked nothing in my name; ask, and you will receive, that your joy may be full"?

NOTES

1. J. W. N. Sullivan, *The Limitations of Science*, (Viking Press, New York, 1953), p. 12.
2. Jacques Ellul, *The Technological System*, (Continuum, New York, 1980), p. 125.
3. *Ibid.*
4. Article in *Horizons of Science*, Ed. Carl F. H. Henry (Harper and Row, New York, 1978), p. 221.
5. Quoted by Peter Ostertund in "Probing the Universe", *Christian Science Monitor*, March 7, 1985.
6. J. S. Polkinghorne, *The Quantum World* (Longman, London and New York, 1984), p. 2.
7. D. Gareth Jones, "Man in the Context of Evolutionary Theory", *Horizons of Science*, p. 43.
8. Sir Fred Hoyle, *The Intelligent Universe* (Holt, Rinehart and Winston, New York, 1984), p. 139.
9. Nicholas Berdyaev, *The Meaning of History* (Geofrey Bles, London, 1945), p. 15.
10. *Horizons of Science*, p. 255.
11. This is the title of an article in *American Journal of Physics*, 52 (10), October, 1954 — now revised and republished in *Transcendence and Providence, Reflections of a Physicist and Priest*, volume 6 in this series.

CHAPTER 3

THE MYSTERY OF MATTER

THE remarkable changes which have taken place in modern science are well illustrated by comparing the understanding of physical matter which prevailed in the 18th and 19th centuries with the view which currently prevails.

Before the dawn of the 20th century it was generally believed that the building blocks of the atom, insubstantial though they might appear to be, were of solid stuff, with their particle behaviour fixed by laws or regularities which could be described in mechanistic terms, and likened, in a crude way, to a kind of billiard ball behaviour. The universe itself was described as an infinitely complex but predictable machine operating in terms of fixed and final laws. Sir Isaac Newton's *Principia Mathematica* asserted that:

> Absolute, true, and mathematical time, of itself, and from its own nature, flows equably without relation to anything external... Absolute space, in its own nature, without relation to anything external, remains always similar and immovable... Absolute motion is the translation of a body from one absolute space into another... Every body continues in its state of rest, or of uniform motion in a straight line, unless it is compelled to change that state by forces imposed upon it.

These physical laws were regarded as final, and the task remaining for natural science was to extend their application and to establish their relationships. So firmly was science fixed in this mechanistic pattern that Joseph Louis Lagrange, the French mathematician, was constrained to deplore the fact that Newton had deprived every successor of the challenge of further physical discovery.

Although Newton himself was a man of deep Christian faith who posited divine control behind the ordering of nature, the scientific materialism which was built on his principles showed no such awareness of dependence on the Almighty, and a religious scepticism, if not outright hostility, generally came to characterize the attitude of 19th century science. The eminent French mathematician, Pierre Simon Laplace, asserted that if it were possible to know the position and the velocity of every particle in the universe, it would be possible to predict all future events. Asked by the emperor Napoleon where the Deity fitted into this neat system he reportedly said, "Je n'ai pas besoin de cette hypothèse."

With the dawn of the 20th century, however, (1905 was the eventful year!) the picture began radically to change, and it changed so rapidly as to shatter within a generation's time the conceptual framework of theoretical physics. By the middle of the present century Newton's magnificent edifice, built with incredible genius, lay ruined. To recognize this fact is not to discredit Sir Isaac Newton. Since the behaviour of molecules remains amenable to statistical averages Newtonian principles remain both valid and essential for operator equations, and without them the spectacular achievements of modern technology would not have been possible.

Relativity theory provided the catalyst for the change. In particle physics it was found that matter and energy are equivalent entities under certain transformations in nature. Experiments conducted over thirty years on the nucleus of the atom disclosed a seemingly endless array of particles — protons, neutrons, positrons, mesons — none of which could be designated as basic. It began to appear that physical matter, as the ancient Greeks had proposed, was infinitely divisible, and that the term elementary particle was a misnomer. Particle physics, instead of finding a basic simplicity in nature, had uncovered endless complexity. Werner Heisenberg remarked: "By getting to smaller and smaller units, we do not come to fundamental units, or indivisible units, but we *do* come to a point where division has no meaning."[1]

In recent years quarks and gluons have become the chief candidates for the role of basic constituents of matter, the quarks (the name is taken from the line in Joyce's *Finnegan's Wake*, "Three quarks for Muster Mark"!) comprising the proton and the neutron in the nucleus of the atom, and the gluons manifesting the forces that hold them together. But these forces are amazingly complex in their relationships, (words used to describe their binding are "up", "down", "strange", "charm", "beauty" and "truth"!) and it remains to be seen whether they furnish the clue to basic particle structure.

The lay person who is overwhelmed by the complexity of all this may be excused for wondering whether the description of matter cannot be reduced to something simpler than particle physics has uncovered, and there appears to be a growing feeling among scientists themselves that physics is approaching a water-shed in its investigations. Richard Morris has summed up the situation thus:

> Theoretical physics is currently trying a somewhat different approach. Attempts are being made to discover a single theory that will explain the four fundamental forces of nature. If this can be done (and the forces don't suddenly begin to multiply the way particles have!), it might be possible to gain some clues as to why particle physics seems to be so complex. It might yet prove to be possible to discern a Copernican simplicity amid the complex interactions engaged in by particles that are produced in modern accelerators.[2]

Up to the present time such Copernican simplicity has eluded physics.

It is tempting to assume that in this break-down of matter the physicist is dealing with some tangible or material substance in the sense in which these words are ordinarily used. What must be recognized is that material analogies and physical descriptions no longer serve the descriptive needs of particle make-up and behaviour. Quarks do not take up any space at all; particles such as the nutrino are suppositions used for mathematical symmetry. "What we observe", wrote Werner Heisenberg, "is not nature itself, but nature exposed to our method of questioning."[3] But the mathematical symmetry and the method of questioning are no longer served by the traditional language and symbolism of classical science. A new esoteric language, intelligible only to the mathematically-informed, has had to be employed to explain what is believed to be going on. Let me briefly enlarge.

Classical physics assumed that the activity of the particle was continuous and could be measured in terms of the traditional calculus. The particles, though identical, were distinguishable; they had their own trajectories, and the investigator could know, in theory at least, both where the electron was (its position) and what it was doing (its momentum). The principle of continuity applied to all physical processes, whether it was heat, light, electromagnetism or gravity. What quantum physics uncovered was a discontinuity in sub-atomic behaviour. There were no trajectories to follow; "here" could not be distinguished from "there". The electrons were not only identical, they were indistinguishable. Max Planck's spectroscopic analysis of the radiation of heated bodies showed that the radiation takes place not continuously, but in small packets which he called "quanta", and Albert Einstein's later experiments showed that a beam of light, instead of constituting a continuous wave, is really a shower of particles or pieces of light which he called "photons". Certain manifestations of this discontinuity were not merely spectacular, but seemingly inconceivable. In his experiments with the photo-electric plate Einstein found that the photon displaces the electron, thus causing its disappearance and replacement. It could be shown, for example, that if an electron were put in a long box where it could travel freely, the electron, under certain circumstances, would sometimes be found at one end of the box, and sometimes at the other end, but *never* in the middle. How did it get from one end to the other? The comic

cartoon in *The New Yorker* of a downhill skier circumna-
vigating both sides of a tree and then continuing blissfully
on his parallel tracks is no more ridiculous than the
behaviour of the sub-atomic particle.

This inescapable random element prevents the simulta-
neous measurement of the particle's positions and
momentum. The investigator has the option of knowing
either the position of the particle or its momentum, but
not both, and — this is the shocker! — since the
measurement of the particle enforces a collapse of the
wave packet the choice of measurement which the
investigator makes decides the particle's behaviour! J. C.
Polkinghorne has said that a basic feature of quantum
theory is "that we know where things are if we actually
look and see. Otherwise they are not locatable".[4]

From the point of view of classical science such particle
behaviour was nonsensical — "a thermodynamic of
unpredictable abandon where no logic resides", as one
physicist described it — and many scientists with
preconceived ideas of what nature could do and could not
do refused to accept the findings of quantum mechanics at
their face value. They believed that there must be
"hidden variables" somewhere which, uncovered, would
provide a "logical" explanation of what was happening.
Albert Einstein, himself one of the intellectual grandfath-
ers of quantum mechanics and the last person in the world
to have preconceived ideas about matter, could not bring
himself to accept the indeterminacy which it implied, and
he separated himself from Max Planck at this point. "God
does not play dice", he insisted. Erwin Schrödinger,
whose work in quantum theory led to the equation which
bears his name, said to Niels Bohr in 1926 that "If we are
going to stick to this damn quantum jumping, then I
regret that I ever had anything to do with quantum
theory".[5] Many physicists, however, including Planck
and Bohr, were convinced that the behaviour of the
particle, however extraordinary it might appear, disclosed
the existing reality, and they concluded that if the
traditional calculus could not explain the seeming para-

dox science had better try to find a mathematics that could. "Don't tell God what to do!", Bohr shot back at Einstein. Hence the search for a quantum field theory. "The story", Polkinghorne writes, "had a happy ending."

> Dirac showed that quantum theory had the remedy for its supposed ills within itself. By consistently applying Maxwell's theory of the electromagnetic field he constructed the first known specimen of a quantum field theory. This provided an example of a well-understood formalism which if interrogated in a particle-like way gave particle behaviour and if interrogated in a wave-like way gave wave behaviour... Since that day of Dirac's discovery the dual nature of light as wave and particle has been free of paradox for those in the know.[6]

Polkinghorne adds that "Mathematics is the perfect language for this sort of exercise and it shows its power by penetrating beyond the everyday dialectic of wave and particle to the synthesis of a quantum field."[7]

The fact that mathematics provides a perfect articulation of wave/particle duality does not mean that it has explained the phenomenon. While there may be no uncertainty about what physics has described the uncertainty over what it means or implies remains. The physicist may choose to ignore this matter. After all, macro events comprise the area in which he and everyone else have to live and do their work, and these events are still entirely predictable. Niels Bohr, preferring to think of quantum theory as simply a calculational procedure, decided to bypass this ontological concern, and his conclusion probably represents the general feeling of most physicists:

> The entire formalism is to be regarded as a tool for deriving predictions, of definite or statistical character, as regards information obtainable under experimental conditions described in classical terms.[8]

In conversation with a friend Bohr declared:

> There is no quantum world. There is only an abstract quantum physical description. It is wrong to think that the task of physics is to find out how nature *is*. Physics concerns what we can say about nature.

While this attitude of philosophical detachment may be quite legitimate for the scientist while he is working in his abstract field it seems to me that it is unacceptable as an epistemic approach to reality. The macro world cannot be separated from its particle substrate. Everything that is physically real relates ultimately to particle make-up and behaviour. The physicist who arbitrarily separates the quantum world from the world of experience is in the position of a bankrupt entrepreneur whom the courts allow to go on living in his accustomed high style while the accountants are trying to straighten out his affairs. The real situation, it seems to me, has been summed up by P. F. Panofsky, former President of the American Physical Society: "Physics has been thrown into a state of maximum confusion at its most basic level."

Quantum uncertainty obviously has significant philosophical implications. They are controversial and are bound to remain open. Let me make one or two observations.

At first glance it may appear tempting to draw the conclusion that the uncertainty principle implies that chance or accident is at work in particle behaviour and that all material events are outside the chain of meaningful cause and effect. "Does an individual quantum event achieve anything more than the toss of a coin?" asks a prominent scientist.[9] Was Bertrand Russell right after all when on allegedly scientific grounds he drew his despairing moral conclusion:

> That man is the product of causes which had no prevision of the end they were achieving; that his origin, his growth, his hopes and fears, his loves and beliefs, are but the outcome of accidental collocations of atoms ... if not quite beyond dispute, are yet so nearly certain, that no philosophy which rejects them can hope to stand.[10]

Uncertainty or unpredictability, however, does not necessarily imply chance or accident, and I do not see that quantum mechanics gives Lord Russell's nihilism its alleged scientific support. The fact is that the unpredictability of the particle turns out to be remarkably creative. By way of illustration: When a negative pi meson collides with a proton, both the pi meson and the proton are destroyed, but in their place two new particles are created — a neutral K meson and the proton of the original collision! The original particles immolate themselves to create new forms which, after a disappearing act, re-emerge in their original state. Talk about magic! There seems to be a lot more here than the toss of a coin.

Some physicists are suggesting that the fact that law and order prevail in nature despite the unpredictable behaviour of its substrate points to an influence that can better be described as noetic than as accidental. Many years ago Sir James Jeans observed "The laws which nature obeys are less suggestive of those which a machine obeys in its motion than those which the musician obeys in writing a fugue, or a poet in composing a sonnet. The motions of electrons and atoms do not resemble those of parts of a locomotive so much as those of dancers in a cotillon."

I should think that the brunt of the critical impact of the new physics is going to have to be absorbed by that philosophy of materialism or mechanistic determinism which dominated modern science well into the present century and remains the practical philosophy of the times. I am aware that scientific materialism is not going to be discredited just because physics discovers that the quark occupies no space or that the electron can be where it isn't (any more than Bishop Berkeley's idealism was discredited by Samuel Johnson's crude kick at a stone!). Professor Gordon H. Clarke has reminded us that:

> The scientist's inability to construct an experiment that can determine both velocity and position surely gives no information on the still unknown laws of infinitesimal particles. Or, for that matter, the scientist's inability leaves uncertain whether nature is constructed of particles at all, or whether it is a continuum. The result is zero, neither positive nor negative.[11]

But if the abandonment by physics of the classical

description of matter does not of itself imply the existence of immaterial spirit or mind it removes the basic support which materialism used to claim for its philosophy of science. It can now be said that physics provides a grounding for freedom of will rather than an attack upon it, and if words and descriptions are to be used meaningfully natural science must now ask itself what support remains in physics for the kind of billiard ball materialism which, a few short years ago, scoffed at a spiritual understanding of life and the world. An eminent Russian writer in an article smuggled out of his country a few years ago challenged the intellectuals of the west to give this philosophical question the seriousness it deserves. In the article the writer quoted an observation made by Alexander Pushkin *seventy years ago*: "One gets the impression that society is now faced with an urgent question — where does truth lie, in idealism or in positivism?" The writer went on to observe that one can understand the reluctance of authorities in a country whose political philosophy rests on materialism to face the implications of the new knowledge, but why the moral equivocation in the west?

Let me close this brief discussion of the mystery of matter with a more positive observation from the same writer:

> Early as it is to draw definite conclusions, I believe an answer of sorts to the question "Where is truth?" is already emerging. Just as the body rejects a foreign implant, there is now in progress a rejection of "positive philosophy" and all its accompanying ideology. Our society is covering it with a scab of scepticism, so that this graft is no longer attached to the living soul as it was seventy or a hundred years ago, but is rejected by it. But that is not enough. We need new spiritual energies, a source of positive influence... We are profoundly convinced that Christianity alone possesses enough moral force gradually to inspire and transform our world. Therefore the only question that remains is how profoundly we succeed in understanding this fact and embodying it in our lives in our time.[12]

NOTES

1. Quoted by Paul Davies, *God and the New Physics* (J. M. Dent and Son, London, 1983), p. 144.
2. William Morris, *Dismantling the Universe* (Simon and Schuster, New York, 1983), pp. 198–9.
3. Werner Heisenberg, *Physics and Philosophy* (Harper and Row, New York, 1958), p. 58.
4. J. C. Polkinghorne, *The Quantum World* (Longman, London and New York, 1984), p. 38.
5. Polkinghorne, p. 53.
6. Polkinghorne, p. 7.
7. Polkinghorne, p. 6.
8. Polkinghorne (see previous note), p. 79, culls these quotations of Niels Bohr from Max Jammer's *The Philosophy of Quantum Mechanics* (John Wiley, 1974).
9. Fred Hoyle, who raises this question in his latest book, *The Intelligent Universe* (Holt and Winston, New York, 1983), answers his question with a challenging affirmation of intelligence in control.
10. Bertrand Russell, "A Free Man's Worship", in *Mysticism, Logic and Other Essays* (Norton, New York, 1929).
11. Gordon H. Clarke, "The Limits and Uses of Science" (Harper and Row, New York, 1978), p. 268.
12. Alexander Solzhenitsyn, *ibid.*, pp. 145, 147.

CHAPTER 4

THE NATURE OF SCIENTIFIC
DISCOVERY

THE popular image of the scientist is that of a person absorbed in the details of his specialized work — Madame Curie toiling in a lab which is full of test tubes, Albert Einstein lost in equations on a chalk board. Early in the 17th century Francis Bacon put forth the view that scientific laws were generalizations drawn from observed facts. The work of the scientist was to perform experiments, analyse the results and then make theoretical deductions from the facts. Experiment and discovery first, then theory and analysis. Bacon's view of scientific method was so influential as to establish something of a norm for the methodology of modern science. According to this popular understanding, shared by many scientists themselves, the quantities of science are solely those which are directly measurable or which have the capability of measurement. Edwin Hubble said, "Not until the empirical resources are exhausted need we pass on to the dreamy realms of speculation."[1]

This modern understanding of scientific method stands in marked contrast to the philosophy of science which prevailed earlier. Science acquired its present limited meaning barely before the nineteenth century. Before that time it was called natural philosophy. In ancient times science was indifferent to experiment and treated technical research with contempt. Aristotle would have nothing to do with experimental demonstration; Plato shunned any kind of compromise with application even in order to further research; Archimedes did invent a machine in order to convince sceptics of the exactitude of his numerical equations, but he ordered it to be destroyed right after the demonstration.

May I suggest that the somewhat arbitrary distinction which has come to be drawn between modern scientific method — a method which admittedly requires material exactitude and experimental proof — and the philosophy of an allegedly "pre-scientific" age which placed little emphasis upon experiment and research, is not quite as valid as is generally supposed, and that by making this distinction between scientific and pre-scientific method we labour under something of a misconception concerning the nature of scientific discovery. The fact is that Bacon's description of scientific method was not accurate even in his own day and it certainly is not today. Necessary as experiment may be for the confirmation of theory it is not through technique that science comes to its most important discoveries. With all due respect to Edwin Hubble the fact remains that in pure science theory itself, even "dreamy speculation", usually comes first with the telescope and the microscope, even the logical analysis, being employed later on in the game. Sir Arthur Eddington used to say, "It is a good rule not to put too much confidence in the observational results that are put forward until they are confirmed by theory."

Let me quote here from a book by Richard Morris, the title of which I have used for the heading of this chapter:

> In all scientific fields, theory is frequently more important than experimental data. Scientists are generally reluctant to accept the existence of a phenomenon when they do not know how to explain it. On the other hand, they will often accept a theory that is especially plausible before there exist any data to support it. This is why Copernicus' heliocentric hypothesis was accepted long before the experiments that confirmed it could be performed.[2]

The chapter from which this paragraph is taken is entitled, "The Primacy of Theory" and draws supporting evidence from the achievements of Copernicus, Galileo, Kepler, Newton and the great scientists of our own time. He cites Johannes Kepler's work as typical. Ignoring the telescope Kepler left it to his co-worker Tycho Brahe to discover the celestial evidence that would support his theoretical laws of planetary motion.

This situation has not changed as far as the requirements of pure science are concerned. The spectacular achievements of the twentieth century rest upon the disinterested theories of men like Clerk Maxwell, Jeans, Eddington, Albert Einstein and Max Planck who, true to the best instincts of their profession sat loose to the technical significance of their discoveries. Einstein's indifference to the urgent attempts of fellow scientists to "prove" relativity theory exemplifies the orientation of the pure scientist. Einstein's absent-mindedness was more than a caricature.

Essential to scientific discovery is a kind of intuitive grasp of reality, an inner apprehension, which, far from being inimical to the exactitude which science requires, gives it its needed conceptual support. If science were to lose this disinterestedness, as appears to be happening, the ultimate consequences for scientific discovery would be disastrous. "Pure logic could never lead us to anything but tautologies", wrote the French physicist Henri Poincaré. "It would create nothing new; not from it alone can any science issue".[3]

The fact that modern science is linked inextricably with mathematics does not change this basic orientation. Mathematics itself cannot be isolated from the intuitive apprehension of reality. Let me briefly enlarge.

For most of us mathematics is thought of as a precise and factual discipline which has nothing whatever to do with inward thought and feeling. Its logic is true and universal. Precisely for this reason it lends itself to the requirements of scientific discovery. Two plus two will always have to make four whatever the scientist may feel about it; the sum of the angles of a triangle will always and everywhere add up to one hundred and eighty degrees regardless of who is looking at it.

Before the turn of the century, however, pure mathematics was beginning to have some doubts about these absolutes. The loss of certainty which was about to overtake physics was already affecting mathematics. From Immanuel Kant there had come prestigious support for an "intuitionist" appreciation of mathematics, a recognition that mathematics, being itself an activity of the human mind, was, like all other activities of the self-conscious spirit, independent of the material world. Philosophers maintained that human selectivity undergirds logic; it is the human mind which chooses the postulates which are consistent with one another. Because the scale of human observation is always relative the resulting image of reality, even the logic of it, will have to be relative. Let me use a simple illustration from every day experience. Seen by one who is about to shave the edge of a razor blade is a continuous, hard, straight line; viewed under a microscope it is rough and tortuous; in the chemist's lab it is seen to be composed of loose atoms of carbon and iron; the physicist, for his part, finds these atoms in an electronic state of perpetual motion. The scales of human observation have determined the kind of reality that is going to be uncovered. Does this relativity apply only to material things like atoms? What about immaterial concepts themselves, concepts of geometry and arithmetic? Does a kind of conceptual relativity apply there also? If, for example, my understanding of space should require universal curvature, what happens to the reality of a geometry requiring straight lines? The geometry based upon the requirement of straight lines will still be conceptually useful and it will remain essential to experimental and theoretical science, but how will it relate to the nature of ultimate reality? Gödel's incompleteness theorem, I believe, has something to say concerning the relativity of arithmetic at this point.

To the logical positivists considerations like these were nonsense, an "intuitive logic" being a contradiction in terms. Ably led by Bertrand Russell the positivists argued that in mathematics logic rules quite independent of the mind of the investigator. Thus was the issue joined at the turn of the century.

Looking back on this philosophical controversy it is fascinating to see that an issue which seemed to be of merely academic interest a century ago was to prove of very practical relevance to the emerging needs of physical science — another instance of that remarkable concurrence found so often in areas of investigation when people tunnelling from different directions come upon each other in the conceptual depths. While philosophers were engaged in this esoteric discussion of logic versus intuition a number of physicists of the first rank were speculating along similar lines. When it became apparent that some of the discoveries of the new physics could not be meshed with the traditional requirements of the calculus some of them began to ask whether there might not be conceived a different kind of calculus to accommodate the new learning. Max Planck and Albert Einstein, in particular, began to look around for something more flexible than Newtonian measurement and Aristotelian logic to account for the way matter was behaving. The developments which followed, to which I referred briefly in the preceding chapter, may be said to be something of a vindication of the intuitionists.

Einstein found that the more powerful tools which he needed for his gravitational theory were available in the geometry of George Bernhard Riemann and in the mathematics of the tensor calculus worked up by M. G. Ricci and T. Levi-Civita. Riemann was a student of Karl Frederick Gauss the mathematician who, as early as the year 1813 had voiced his doubt that Euclid's parallel axiom could be proved deductively from his other axioms. Gauss then projected a kind of non-Euclidian geometry which Riemann further developed. Riemann's geometry was not limited to merely three dimensions but allowed for any number of dimensions. Einstein in his general theory of relativity related a four-dimensional space/time continuum to Riemann's openness and introduced material bodies into it — a fantastic *tour de force* of logic projected by an audacious leap of faith! Einstein held, in common with Clerk Maxwell, that "there is an established harmony between human thought and independent empirical reality, in virtue of which the human mind can grasp the rational structures embedded in reality. That is to say, it is only through intuition, resting on sympathetic understanding of experience, that we hope to arrive at the elementary laws which govern the cosmos."[4]

But here the old question comes back to haunt one. What assurance has the scientist that his impressions, whether derived from intuition or from experience, belong to a prospect that is not quite distorted? What the scientist constantly does, of course, is to submit his theories and observations to tests of falsification, revision and reinterpretation after which a body of knowledge emerges which is compatible and coherent. But this very testing itself is an aspect of human conceptualization which takes for granted the possibility of a correspondence with reality. Ultimately the scientist has to rest his theory on what George Santayana called "the soul's invincible surmise".

So impressed was Albert Einstein with this co-relation between the intuitive working of the human mind and the reality he sought to uncover that he gave it an almost religious interpretation. "To the sphere of religion" said Einstein, "belongs the faith that the regulations valid for the world of existence are rational, that is, comprehensible to reason. I cannot conceive of a genuine scientist without profound faith. The situation may be expressed by an image: science without religion is lame, religion without science is blind."[5]

What must be added parenthetically is that Albert Einstein's religious views were related (where they were "rooted" may be another thing!) not so much to the biblical insights of the race to which he belonged as to the pantheistic ideas of another Jew, Baruch Spinoza. Einstein did not think of God as personal but as immanent in the processes of the universe, and he could not bring himself to ascribe to his "Old One" that measure of personal involvement which he found in "the relatedness of the human mind to the physical reality around him". In a telegram cabled to a Jewish newspaper in 1929

Einstein remarked: "I believe in Spinoza's God who reveals himself in the harmony of all that exists, but not in a God who concerns himself with the fate and action of men." Is there not a strange and tragic contradiction here? How can "the fate and action of men" be divorced from "the harmony of all that exists"? When the force of the Nazi horror broke upon his own people Einstein certainly did not allow that distinction to stand. The fact is that Einstein's philosophical and religious views were confused and paradoxical. This became evident in the quantum controversy to which I referred earlier. In his debate with Niels Bohr Einstein seemed to be arguing against himself. Although quantum theory required for its appreciation the very leap of faith which he had made when faced with the challenge of general relativity he refused to make it when confronted with the challenge posed by the uncertainty principle. His reason may have been a good and worthy one — quantum theory seemed to put the regularities of nature outside the chain of cause and effect which Einstein was determined to respect! — but the logic of his resistance was faulted. Jacques Ellul, with characteristic sarcasm, has said: "It is clear that Einstein, extraordinary mathematical genius that he was, was no Pascal... The banality of Einstein's remarks in matters outside his speciality is as astonishing as his genius within it."[6]

This paradox notwithstanding, Einstein's monumental achievement in science was to demonstrate that there could be no clear separation between matter and the laws which govern it, and the impact of this achievement in intuitive logic could hardly be overstated. In quantum mechanics it is now deemed theoretically impossible to eliminate the observer from what is being observed. Increasingly it appears that the structure of the material universe has something in common with the laws which govern the behaviour of the human mind. I believe that a valid inference of modern science is that the universe, far from being an impersonal and an indifferent construct, is responsive to man's intuitive insights; it invites his personal involvement and waits to reward his efforts at understanding. Of this more in chapters VIII and IX where I consider "the uniqueness of man" and "the transcendent self".

Awareness of this human openness in the chain of physical necessity, coupled with the supremacy of a moral order, has tremendous consequences for our own sceptical age. Many people today, possessed of only materialistic conceptions of life, and having been informed that matter is unpredictable in its behaviour, have drawn the conclusion that man is the helpless victim of meaningless events over which he has no control. A kind of fatalism has taken over the institutions of our time and threatens to destroy all that has been achieved over the centuries through faith and intuition.

Surely at this point religion and science should be making a loud and concerted moral protest: "I call heaven and earth to record this day against you, that I have set before you life and death, blessing and cursing; therefore choose life, that both thou and thy seed may live." (Deuteronomy 30.19)

The Christian theologian has the responsibility to go beyond this moral protest and underline the biblical insistence that man bears the image of God, and that the spiritual awareness which he possesses relates to the Reality which is at the heart of all being. The theologian should feel no embarrassment about doing this, because it is becoming daily more evident that human knowledge is not going to bring man to an understanding of the truth of life and being without the sustaining evidence of faith.

NOTES

1. Jastrow, *op.cit.*, p. 63.
2. Richard Morris, *The Nature of Scientific Discovery*, p. 114.
3. See K. C. Cole, "The Scientific Aesthetic", in *Discovery*, December 1983, p. 63.
4. T. F. Torrance, *Christian Theology and Scientific Culture* (Belfast, 1980), p. 57.
5. *ibid.*, p. 58.
6. Jacques Ellul, *The Technological Society* (Vantage Press, New York, 1964), p. 435.

CHAPTER 5

LIGHT AND LIFE

IN chapter III I looked at nature from the point of view of its particle make-up and behaviour. When we turn from the study of that which is infinitesimally small to consider the behaviour of matter in a universe which is inconceivably large we find ourselves in a realm no less mysterious. The basic form of energy in the universe is light. Relativity theory deals with its action and here, as in quantum behaviour, the investigator finds himself led beyond physics into metaphysics.

In 1905 Albert Einstein published his paper "On the Electrodynamics of Moving Bodies". The publication of this paper is rightly regarded as marking the great divide between the classical physics of the eighteenth and nineteenth centuries and the "new physics" of the twentieth century. Well before the turn of the century, however, there were spectacular developments in science which proved to be not unrelated to Einstein's epochal work. In the latter half of the nineteenth century James Clerk Maxwell pioneered his conception of the dynamic field as an independent reality within which matter, force and field were integrated, and Clerk Maxwell's equations were to have significant implications for relativity theory.[1] In the year 1887 two American physicists, Albert Michelson and Edward Morley made the astounding discovery that there is no difference in the speed of light regardless of the direction in which it moves or the point from which it is observed. This experiment served to confirm conclusions which Einstein had reached independently, and, seizing upon the hypothesis put forward by Hendrik Lorentz and George James Fitzgerald that the length of a moving object shortens in the direction of its motion, Einstein declared that time and space were relative to the constant value of light. That is to say, they were not the absolute and independent entities which Newtonian physics had assumed them to be. His 1905 paper succeeded in proving that the mass of a body increases with its motion, and he contended that if the body were ever to attain the speed of light its mass would become infinite. Mass and energy, he declared, were equivalent and interconvertible. Hence, the ominous equation $E = mc^2$.

Einstein's theory of 1905, the theory of special relativity, dealt only with motion at a constant speed in a straight line. In order to take curvature into account he had to expand his theory, having recourse to ideas that were far more radical than physics had previously encountered and far more complex mathematically. What he did, in effect, was to eliminate the idea of gravity as a "force", and to substitute the sophisticated idea that gravity is a property of the geometrical structure of the universe. The eminent British mathematician, the late Sir Edmund Whittaker, summed it up tersely: "Gravitation represents a continual tendency of the universe to straighten itself out. This is General Relativity in a single sentence." Up to this time most scientists had assumed that the universe was already straightened out celestially and that gravity was pulling things inward. Einstein showed that the presence of matter produces curvature in space/time, and that this curvature induces bodies to move as if they were attracted by a "force" of gravity. Actually the force is not there at all. It is the distortion of matter which is giving gravity its pull.

Here in relativity theory, as in Quantum mechanics, we find ourselves in a realm the calculus of which is incomprehensible to the lay person, and most of us have no alternative but to take the scientist's word for it. But whether we are knowledgeable or not, the appreciation of relativity theory requires a mental orientation far removed from the thought-forms of classical physics which conceived of space and time as independent constants.

Einstein established that the speed of light is the invariant.

Obviously the word relativity itself is somewhat misleading. There is nothing relative about light; the relativity is with the observer in his space/time nexus. Einstein at one time considered calling his theory "Invariance Theory". Light, we are told, is possibly the most basic entity of the physical universe, representing the fundamental form of radiation in the electromagnetic field. From it all the matter in the universe appears to have come by a process of what physicists call pair creation. All forces in the universe are governed by its speed. The behaviour of light defies preconceived logic. It travels where there is no medium (relativity theory sentenced the ether to oblivion!); it never rests and its speed is constant (if it appears to have slowed down it is because time has slowed!); it is invisible (what we see are the effects of light, not light itself); while light moves through the universe on its independent, ordered, timeless, endless and invisible way it is absorbed and converted into other forms of energy which comprise the physical reality to which "time-bound" man can relate. T. F. Torrance writes:

> In virtue of its nature light has a supreme place among physical realities in the universe, and in virtue of its unparalleled speed a unique role in linking and co-ordinating them all together within its rational harmony. In this way through the discovery of light by reference to which the whole space-time framework of empirical reality is to be understood, modern physics has brought us to the conception of the universe as *a universe of light*.[2]

One cannot help but notice the remarkable affinity here between the determining role of light in the physical universe and its central place in religious thought and experience. From primitive expressions in sun worship to mystical insights like those of St. John of the Cross the imagery of light has served to express the divine afflatus. The remarkable qualities of light which were noted above — as invisible, unapproachable, timeless, unmediated —

are the attributes ascribed to divinity. The initial statement of the Bible (Genesis 1. 1–4) fixes God's first
creative act as the projection of light from the void: "The
earth was without form and void, ... and God said, 'Let
there be light! and there was light.'" Admittedly the
framework of this Genesis saga is far-removed from the
cosmology of modern science; nevertheless the assertion
remains basic: "I create light and darkness, ... I the Lord
do these things" (Isaiah 45.7).

It is tempting for the scholar to want to use this biblical
analogy of light simply in a metaphorical way — a kind of
poetic expression of a spiritual insight which is inexpres-
sible. The New Testament, however, seems to require
more than analogical thought at this point. The New
Testament goes far beyond any spiritual generalization to
give light particular, even physical refinement, in relation
to the being of Jesus Christ. The Apostle Paul for whom
the Damascus Road experience was very real and factual,
says that "The same God who commanded the light to
shine out of darkness hath shined in our hearts to give the
light (*photisma*) of the knowledge of the glory of God in
the face of Jesus Christ" (2. Cor. 4.6); and the fourth
Evangelist speaks of "the true light which lighteth every
man that cometh into the world" (John 1.4,9). This
refinement of life and light in Jesus Christ is the
distinctive aspect of the Christian faith which separates it
from all general religious views of life and the world.[3]

Many scientists and philosophers have rejected Christianity allegedly because of this scandal of particularity.
They find it intellectually offensive to be asked to believe
that the Godhead, if there is a Godhead, should distil his
pure being in the frame and form of a historical person,
Jesus of Nazareth. Einstein's telegram of 1929 quoted in
the previous chapter typifies this position. The scandal of
particularity, however, does not appear so objectionable
when we perceive that in his incarnation in Jesus Christ
God is doing the very thing which science says has to be
done if light is to be operative. It has to be transmuted.
Since God in his pure being is ineffable only an

incarnation can serve the human need. "No man hath seen God at any time. The only begotten son which is in the bosom of the Father, he hath declared him" (John 1.18).

Just in passing let me say that physics itself is hardly in a position to deplore the scandal of particularity in the Christian faith. Atomic phenomena show an even more scandalous particularity in the energizing of light. All the crucial activities of modern science are based on the seemingly impossible phenomenon whereby individual atoms are "charged" and "made manifest" by the giving up of an electron. The improbability of this happening is illustrated by the fact that out of every fifty thousand million million molecules (1 to 50³) only one loses an electron! W. F. G. Swann has said: "The emission of light goes on everywhere. The photoelectric effect is continually operative in the economy of plant life; and yet, from the point of view of the actual things which are the seat of this phenomena, from the point of view of the atom, the phenomena themselves are of such a rarity that no less drastic a word than 'miracle' is fit to describe them."[4] The improbability of God manifesting himself in a single member of his humanity is far less remote than the probability of the molecule ever doing what science accepts as routine.

A further theological observation, not unrelated to what I have already said, has to do with the distinction between appearance and reality, the subtle interplay of "things that are seen and things that are not seen". In the Bible there is no denial, as in some religions, of the reality of the visible world. The things that are seen are certainly real, but they are temporal and belong to an order that is of relative significance. They are under the control and in the service of a higher will whose disclosures are made to the understanding of faith. "By faith we know that the worlds were framed by the word of God, so that what is seen was made out of things which do not appear" (Hebrews 11.3).

As long as science equated the disclosure of reality with

a stultifying materialism it was not easy to posit the reality of an invisible world which was under the determination of the Word of God. But the picture has changed. Reality, even physical reality, is a very subtle thing, and it appears to be energized by unapproachable light. In converting to mass or rest energy, that is to say, the kind of energy which man can touch and handle and see, it humbles itself; it accommodates itself to man's creatureliness. But the energy which is ultimately in control of things is liberated matter.

There is a theological sequel here which cannot be ignored. Any theology which is faithful to the New Testament must affirm the fallen state of man and the alienation of the physical universe from its Creator. The material world, turned in upon itself, awaits deliverance from its material bondage. The apostle Paul insisted that man and nature are presently suspended in "futility" awaiting the deliverance that can only come from "the revealing of the sons of God".

> We know that the whole creation has been groaning in travail until now; and not only the creation, but we ourselves, who have the first fruits of the Spirit, groan inwardly as we wait for adoption as sons, the redemption of our bodies (Romans 8.22, 23).

This theme of man's and nature's fall from grace has been anything but congenial to the temper of modern science. Despite its disclaimer to make qualitative judgements science has held tenaciously to the moral philosophy of perfectibility which characterized the spirit of the Enlightenment in the seventeenth and eighteenth centuries. Although this doctrine has long since exhausted itself intellectually the practical achievements made possible by the techniques of science have sustained its appeal. The rationale of modern science, strikingly evident when the universities are making their pitch for grants to support scientific research, is that man and his world are here to be perfected.

Sometimes this bias assumes a form that is as obnoxious as it is absurd. I think, for example, of the "intriguing prospect" which Professor Paul Davies holds out to us in his book *God and the New Physics*:

> In a universe with virtually unlimited time available for technological enterprise, can we confidently rule out *anything* that is consistent with the laws of physics? During the last few thousand years humans have progressed from technology on the scale of hand tools a few centimeters in size to major engineering projects (bridges, tunnels, dams, cities) many miles in size. If that trend is extrapolated, even at a greatly diminished pace, the time will come when the whole Earth, the solar system, and eventually the stars will be "technologized". The galaxy itself could be remodelled by manipulation, stars moved out of their orbits, created from gas clouds, or destroyed by engineered instabilities. Black holes could be formed or controlled at will as energy sources and/or disposal devices for the effluents of cosmic society. And if galaxies, why not the universe?[5]

Why not indeed? I am constrained to add that Paul Davies' prospect of bridges, tunnels, dams and cities extrapolated into the galaxies is not quite the cosmic fulfilment which the other Paul had in mind when he wrote of "the revealing of the sons of God". (It is not without significance that modern science invariably thinks of future "progress" in technological rather than moral and spiritual terms!) In fairness to Davies it might be added that the intriguing prospect which he put before the reader was coupled with a supposition concerning intelligent control of the universe — a subject which seems to be of increasing interest to science! — and the reader has the feeling that his technological projections were made more for sensational appeal than for scientific credibility.

Physics knows better than this. Physics knows that there is no question about the ultimate deterioration of the physical universe. The scenario varies, and scientists have not yet quite made up their minds whether the universe is fated to expand into infinity with its receding matter so attenuated as to render life insupportable, or whether it is doomed to fall back in upon itself in a condensation so intense as to imprison even light itself. Of course, all this is academic. Long before these unhappy alternatives transpire the solar system will have lost all semblance to present reality. Man has not a ghost of a chance of transcending his material environment. Why should he want to? "The years of our life are threescore and ten, or even by reason of strength fourscore; yet their span is but toil and trouble; they are soon gone, and we fly away" (Psalm 90.10).

These prospects confronting man and his world present a paradox of the utmost irony. Increasingly science is coming to respect the biblical view that man has a unique and perhaps determining role in the cosmos; the universe appears to have been made for man, and not man for the universe. Nevertheless the universe is out to get man. Modern science has no calculus of redemption to deal with this dilemma.

At this point Christian theology assumes a particular relevance for modern man. In and through the action of God in Jesus Christ there takes place that transmutation of light and life which enables man to transcend the world and the universe. Jesus Christ has already descended into hell's black hole and emerged therefrom triumphant over sin and death. On the other side of that triumph Jesus Christ has ascended into the expanding heavens "far above all rule and power and authority and dominion, and above every name that is named, not only in this age but in that which is to come" (Ephesians 1.21). This achievement of God in Jesus Christ is no victory isolated from the human predicament. Jesus Christ is the representative man, the prototype or the first-fruits of the humanity which the incarnation embraces and for whom the victory of grace has been achieved. No conceivable fate awaiting the world and the universe can vitiate this cosmic achievement of God in Jesus Christ. Because of this achievement the whole creation is now oriented to a fulfilment of light and life in which "the creation itself will be set free from its bondage to decay, and obtain the glorious liberty of the children of God" (Romans 8.19–21).

There are other tangents of Christian theology which might profitably be explored in the context of relativity theory and quantum mechanics. I shall enlarge on one of them in chapter VII where I consider "Man and Time". But I have singled out these particular aspects of the biblical revelation to underline its relevance to the science of our time. We are told repeatedly that the Bible is not a book of science and that its concern is with other things. Insofar, however, as these other things have to do with the reality of life and the world they have a very significant bearing upon science. Where this appears to be the case it seems to me that the intellectual community has responsibility to assess the material relevance and worth of this witness.

NOTES

1. See the edition by T. F. Torrance of James Clerk Maxwell, *A Dynamical Theory of the Electromagnetic Field*, Scottish Academic Press, Edinburgh, 1982.
2. T. F. Torrance, *Christian Theology and Scientific Culture*, p. 74.
3. John Calvin expressed this admirably when he said that "the appreciation of faith is not confined to our knowing that there is a God, but chiefly consists in our understanding what is his disposition toward us. For it is not of so much importance to us to know what he is in himself as what he is willing to be to us. We find, therefore, that faith is a knowledge of the will of God respecting us." *Institutes of the Christian Religion*, Book III, Ch. 2.
4. W. G. F. Swann, *The Architecture of the Universe*, (Macmillan, New York. 1934). pp. 55–58.
5. Paul Davies, *God and the New Physics* (London and Melbourne, 1983), p. 207.

CHAPTER 6

EVOLUTION — A THEORY IN TROUBLE

THE story, no doubt apocryphal, belongs to the late nineteenth century, and is attributed to the wife of a bishop of Durham. Hearing in the palace drawing room for the first time of Charles Darwin's theory of evolution she exclaimed to an agitated friend: "Descended from the apes, my dear! Let us hope that it is not true." Then, after a thoughtful pause, "But if it is, let us pray that it does not become generally known!"

The theory of evolution did become generally known, and for over a century the western world has been living with the social and moral, not to say, religious consequences of Darwin's hypothesis. Of course no responsible biologist believes today, if he ever did, that man simply "descended from the apes". The theory was never that simple. Nevertheless the general assumption got abroad that man had merely a natural origin, and it is this impression, divorced from the larger realities of his biological existence, which has had a devastating effect on man's understanding of human nature and its destiny.

It is tragic that the issue developed as it did. Biology has a clear and essential role in science. The role of science in this area is to select the physically calculable elements or the biological properties of living things and to determine their material connections. The physiologist abstracts living forms of matter and isolates their sequences on a linear time frame. Fossil and molecular charts trace human development in relation to other species, like or unlike the human species. Special evolution or microevolution involves changes that can be observed to occur in living species of animals and plants over a limited period of time.

In the next chapter I shall point out the inadequacy from both a philosophical and a scientific point of view of this linear time frame which the biologist is forced to use. It is difficult, however, to see how the scientist can get out from under it in studying the material relationship of living things, and with these abstract and specialized studies religion should have no quarrel.

It is interesting to recall that Charles Darwin himself, at least at the outset of his career, felt that there was no religious problem here. In correspondence in the spring of the year 1876 with Rabbi Naphtali Lewery of Poland, Darwin expressed entire sympathy with the rabbi's view that the controversial theory of evolution was consonant with the Hebrew tradition of creation. Darwin, acknowledging that some religious people found fault with his theory wrote: "But I tell them I only state scientific truths as I have discovered them, and I leave it to the theologians to reconcile them with the Scriptures; that is their province, not mine."

Where recognition is made that biology deals with life at a different level of significance than the religious level there need be no conflict between the disciplines. A biological description of the origin and development of human life no more does away with a religious description than a religious description does away with a biological description. To describe an apparent connection between contingent events is not to explain them, and *much of the difficulty that has arisen over evolution has resulted from the mistake of confusing how a thing works with what it is.*

Helpful in this regard is a whimsical piece of correspondence between theologian Karl Barth and his grandniece Christine. In a letter to Christine who had written her uncle in some perplexity over evolution Barth replied:

> Has no one explained to you in your seminar that one can as little compare the biblical creation story and a scientific theory like that

of evolution as one can compare, shall we say, an organ and a vacuum-cleaner — that there can be as little question of harmony between them as of contradiction?

The creation story is a witness to the beginning or becoming of all reality distinct from God in the light of God's later acts and words relating to his people Israel — naturally in the form of a saga or poem. The theory of evolution is an attempt to explain the same reality in its inner nexus — naturally in the form of a scientific hypothesis.

The creation story deals only with the becoming of all things, and therefore with the revelation of God, which is inaccessible to science as such. The theory of evolution deals with what has become, as it appears to human observation and research and as it invites human interpretation. Thus one's attitude to the creation story and the theory of evolution can take the form of an either/or only if one shuts oneself off completely either from faith in God's revelation or from the mind (or opportunity) for scientific understanding.

So tell the teacher concerned that she should distinguish what is to be distinguished and not shut herself off completely from either side.[1]

Barth's illustration of the organ and the vacuum cleaner as similar mechanical constructs which have vastly different material functions is to the point. (The distinction might be kept in mind today by computer analysts who liken the working of the human brain with the circuitry of the silicon chip!).

What happens, however, when respect for differentiation is lacking? Suppose Christine's teacher should tell Christine that the principles which apply to the construction and operation of the vacuum cleaner and the wind organ exhaust the principles of design, and that the mechanical processes which they share in common are the only processes which exist? Unfortunately this is precisely the assumption which many evolutionists have made. Consider, for example, the following statement which Jacques Monod, a Nobel prize winner made in his B.B.C. interview of July, 1971: "Everything can be reduced to simple, obvious, mechanical interactions. The animal is a machine and there is no difference at all between men and animals" (sic!). *The New Encyclopedia Britannica* informs us that "Evolution is accepted by all biologists and natural selection is recognized as its cause". The Encyclopedia adds that natural selection is "automatic with no room for divine guidance or design". When a view of man is thus reduced to physical and chemical constituents *and nothing more* it cannot be said that respect is being held for the evidence that belongs to other fields. This sort of thing has happened too often in biological studies. General evolution or "evolutionism" has become a speculative affair with sweeping generalizations being made about the presumed interrelationship of living things. The assumption of the evolutionists that the life which originated and developed by natural means has neither purpose nor control to its design presents a problem not only to religious fundamentalists but to all people who would deal seriously with the meaning and purpose of life. This naturalistic and materialistic explanation of life, propounded to the exclusion of all else, has had a desolating effect on conclusions which have been reached in fields of sociology, anthropology, psychology and the natural sciences. All these areas need to work with a total view of man, and they have not had it. In America today to give a serious theological account of creation is to violate the principle of separation of Church and State — a principle which has become a sacred cow of educationists and legislators, and is invoked at the expense of scientific truth and objectivity.

The time is overdue to challenge some of the basic presuppositions of the evolutionists. This must now be done in the name of science as well as of theology, for if general evolution is in trouble, as indeed it is, it is not because religious fundamentalists have turned against it but because evolutionism itself can no longer, in the name of science, sustain some of its sweeping generalizations.

Darwinian evolution has based its theory on the twin foundations of natural selection: survival of the fittest, and chance mutations. It has failed, however, to establish these presuppositions on experimental evidence. It has not been established who the fittest are whom nature selects to survive. The late C. H. Waddington wrote: "The general principle of natural selection merely means that the individuals who leave most offspring are the ones who leave most offspring." As for chance mutations, the word "chance" denotes the inexplicable, but the very purpose of science is to explain. "A theory that claims to explain with one foot on a tautology and the other in an explanatory void is in trouble."[2]

This isn't quite the way Charles Darwin himself intended it. In his *Origin of Species* Darwin acknowledged that the abrupt manner in which whole groups of species suddenly appear presented a challenge to his theory, but he assumed that evidence would be forthcoming to support the theory of natural selection. That evidence has not appeared, and apparently it is not going to appear. Evolutionist Niles Eldredge has bluntly said: "The pattern that we were told to find for the past one hundred and twenty years does not exist."[3]

Evolutionists have sought to get around the difficulty presented by the non-appearance of traditional forms by postulating quantum speciation or mutations. But again, where is the evidence? Scientists in their attempt to produce new and improved species have bombarded many forms of life with intense radiation designed to speed up the change process, and they have succeeded in developing variations within a given species; but in no case has an alteration of species resulted. A dog is still a dog however his species may have altered.

But even if evidence were forthcoming in the way of supplying the needed missing links in speciation, what would that show? Such evidence would simply show that a chance mutation is not a matter of chance but of cause and effect. Physical science stands or falls on the principle of causality; the introduction of probability into the evolutionist's description constitutes the one case in which, as physicist William Pollard has pointed out, "science expressly renounces an explanation in terms of natural causes".[4]

But all of this is rather academic. The fact is that from what we now know of life's natural processes both the origin of life and its subsequent development into humanoid forms is rendered utterly preposterous simply by chance working. The evolutionists ask us to believe that at some moment in time a simple protein formed by chance in the primordial chemical soup. The computer tells us that in order for a simple protein to form accidentally the chances are 10/42 (forty two noughts after the figure of one). Significant organic changes require that component developments occur simultaneously and independently in bones, nerves, muscles, arteries and the like. These requirements escalate the demand on probability theory astronomically. It would be like having 26 come up simultaneously on 10 or 15 roulette tables in the same casino, followed by all the tables reporting 27, 28 and 29 in lockstep progression. Professor Pierre Grasse who for thirty years held the chair in evolution at the Sorbonne has written: "The probability of dust carried by the wind reproducing Dürer's 'Melancholia' is less infinitesimal than the probability of copy errors in the DNA molecules leading to the formation of the eye; besides, these errors had no relationship whatsoever with the function that the eye would have to perform or was starting to perform."[5] Grasse adds sarcastically that, "There is no law against daydreaming, but science must not indulge in it."

It is this kind of factual knowledge which has led Sir Fred Hoyle, an agnostic of Christian background, and his co-worker, Professor Chandra Wickramasinghe, an atheist Buddhist, to reject as unscientific the theory of gradual evolution by natural selection. "I am one hundred percent certain", said Wickramasinghe, "that life could not have started spontaneously on earth".

Nor is Darwinism going to be rescued by turning from fossil evidence to molecular biology. Chemical evolution is the "in" thing today, and many exponents of molecular biology are still wedded to a purely naturalistic explanation of life's origin and development. They assume that pre-biotic changes in the earth gave rise to the first organisms by purely natural means. Since there is no definitive evidence of what happened at the initial stage, these pre-biotic changes have to be assumed. Dr. H. F. C. Crick himself has acknowledged that the intriguing search for the origin of life on earth will continue to invite "ingenious fabrications of the mind". Given the initial fact of life, however, chemistry proceeds successfully with its investi-gative work. "Nature" using the alphabet of the amino acids, "constructs" a huge range of proteins from combina-tions of a couple dozen amino acids. In this chemical mix there seems to be "preferred structures" and a degree of "self orienting" in the assembly. The genetic information carried in these molecular constructs "decides" what will emerge in the developing life forms. The process appears to be "non-random" with a kind of "blueprint" for "self-assembly" which traces back to the very atoms which form the precursors of the amino acids. With the blueprint thus provided for the entire process from atom to the first living cells, evolution "proceeds" to elaborate its primitive living material into sophisticated life forms.

I have purposely underlined some of the words above in order to illustrate the degree of question-begging which takes place in this allegedly naturalistic "explana-tion" of the origin and development of life processes. No one is calling in question these amazing chemical and physical processes or arguing the remarkable sequences. But to describe them is not to explain them. Indeed the very sophistication of the constructs demands something more than a naturalistic explanation. What is astonishing here is the failure of biochemistry to posit the kind of purposiveness which the presence of the DNA template presupposes. Half a century ago Alexis Carrel in his book, *Man, the Unknown*, illustrated the drama which is involved in the chemical processes of cell construction:

> An organ ... is not made of extraneous material, like a house. Neither is it a cellular construction, a mere assemblage of cells. It is, of course, composed of cells, as a house is of bricks. But it is born

from a cell, as if the house originated from one brick, a magic brick that would set about manufacturing other bricks. Those bricks, without waiting for the architect's drawings or the coming of the bricklayers, would assemble themselves and form the walls. They would also metamorphose into windowpanes, roofing-slates, coal for heating, and water for the kitchen and the bathroom. An organ develops by means such as those attributed to fairies in the tales told to children in bygone times. It is engendered by cells which, to all appearance, have a knowledge of the future edifice, and synthesize from substances contained in blood plasma the building material and even the workers.

Is it naiveté on the part of the religious believer to perceive in these amazing findings of biology, paleontology and chemistry a remarkable illustration of the manner in which "The Lord gave the word" (Psalm 68.11), and, having given it, sustains the world, "by the power of his might" (Ephesians 6.10)? The self-fulfilling "word" of the DNA molecule corresponds remarkably to the creative and self-fulfilling action which the prophet Isaiah ascribed to the work of the Almighty: "So shall my word be that goeth forth from my mouth. It shall not return unto me void but shall accomplish that which I please, and prosper in the thing whereto I send it" (Isaiah 55.11).

Those of us who perceive theological meaning in these areas of study recognize that the sciences have their own specialized language to describe their investigations, and we have no right to expect them to use proof texts from the Bible in the semantics of natural science. It is gratifying, however, to discover that the exact language which they are forced to use no longer runs counter to what the believer considers the witness of the Word of God. I think, for example, of the interesting observation of Sir Fred Hoyle (alleged agnostic) and Dr. Chandra Wickramasinghe (alleged atheist) made in their latest book *Evolution From Space*: "Once we see ... that the probability of life originating at random is so utterly minuscule as to make it absurd, it becomes sensible to think that the fundamental properties of physics, on which life depends, are in every way, deliberate".[6]

NOTES

1. *Karl Barth's Letters, 1961–1968* (Wm. B. Eerdmans, Grand Rapids, Michigan, 1981), p. 184.
2. Huston Smith, *Beyond the Post-Modern Mind* (Crossroads Press, New York, 1982).
3. From a remark made to a Chicago Convention.
4. William G. Pollard, "Critique of Jacques Monod's *Chance and Necessity*" (Soundings, Winter 1973).
5. Pierre Grasse, *Evolution for Living Organisms* (Academic Press, 1971) — cited from *The Christian Century*.
6. In his recent book, *The Intelligent Universe* (Holt, 1984), pp. 12–81, Fred Hoyle takes further aim at Darwinian evolutionism which he considers to be a mathematical impossibility.

CHAPTER 7

MAN AND TIME

IN the last chapter I touched on some of the material difficulties which confront the general theory of evolution. One problem, however, central to any consideration of the development of forms of life and matter is far more critical than the material concerns which I have just considered. It is the problem of *time*. Time has always presented a philosophical challenge; it now presents a scientific challenge as well.

All studies of life and matter, and the understanding of history itself, are based upon connections between contingent events which presuppose a framework of measurable linear time, the progression of which is from the past to the future. Carl Friedrich von Weizsäcker has remarked that "There is not even a meaning of the word *experience* which would not presuppose the distinction between past and future".[1] But it is right here that a serious problem presents itself to science today. Physics finds that the traditional frame of rigid space and absolute time no longer supports the concepts which relativity theory, quantum mechanics and cosmology require for understanding the make-up and behaviour of things physical.

According to relativity theory space and time no longer make the rules. Everything is governed by the speed of light. This requires that the universe be viewed no longer in terms of fixed space — a "here" and a "there"; and in terms of absolute time — a "now" and a "then", but in terms of a dynamic and flexible space/time continuum with space and time having significant degrees of interchangeability. Albert Einstein in one of his last remarks, made on the passing of a friend, said: "For us the distinction between past, present and future is only an illusion, even if a stubborn one."

Quantum mechanics, for its part, has forced physics to entertain the possibility of time reversal. One of the scandalous implications of quantum theory is the possibility of the "present" and "future" determination of events that may have "already" transpired. John Archibald Wheeler writes: "The quantum principle shows that there is a sense in which what the observer will do in the future defines what happens in the past — even in a past so remote that life did not then exist."[2]

Modern theories of cosmology serve further to confound our temporal preconceptions. If, as apparently happened in the singularity at the burst of creation, the event exceeded the speed of light, all physical laws break down, and the very existence of space/time is rendered inconceivable. How does one even talk about a time when there was no time, or a reality without location? We are in the Mad Hatter's world.

Such considerations require a shift in conceptual thinking which is more difficult for the scientist than for the philosopher. Inconceivable, however, as the whole thing seems to be, apparently the laws of the new physics make provision for gear shifting here, and if the scientist wishes to engage the mathematical clutch he can slow down his time machine or speed it up, keep it stationary at a singularity or even reverse it. Fred Hoyle in *The Intelligent Universe* — a book which is not designed to undo his reputation as an exciting maverick! — reminds his fellow scientists that in the equations of Clerk Maxwell which play a crucial role in physics, there is the generally-overlooked provision for "another set of situations with radiation travelling from future to past... So far as Maxwell's laws are concerned, the second set is just as good as the first".[3] Hoyle goes on to suggest that if events were known to operate not only from the past to future but from future to past the seemingly intractable problem of quantum uncertainty would be solved:

Instead of living matter becoming more and more disorganized, it could react to quantum signals from the future — the information necessary for the development of life. Instead of the Universe being committed to increasing disorder and decay, the opposite could then be true.

Obviously if the specialist finds these waters deep to wade in it is foolhardy for the lay person to attempt to ford them. The reason I have stepped in here is not to fathom the depths of physics at this crossing but to feel the changing temperature. We are no longer in the climate of Sir Isaac Newton's time. Nor of Charles Darwin's! As the findings of the new physics filter down to levels of conceptual understanding they will force a look at assumptions which have long been taken for granted. The implications of this for theories of knowledge in general and for evolution in particular are sobering. I venture the suggestion that if Albert Einstein's century had "preceded" — how does one escape linear terminology? — Charles Darwin's, the latter's findings and speculations might not have gained quite the prestige which they did. The challenge confronting natural science as it leaves the twentieth century behind it is to free its understanding from the rigidities of classical laws and theories which have consigned man and nature to material conceptions of space and a linear view of time.

This challenge cannot be separated from the human situation because it is in man himself that the mystery of time focuses. By man I mean the individual person, not generic man, not society. It is the individual human being who exercises a determination over time, fixing its reality vis-à-vis his own being. He relegates to the past the time which he no longer experiences, and he postpones for future materialization the time he has not yet reached.

What is it that thus renders man's own being so decisive for the reality of time? Literally so "momentous"? This determination of time by the individual is exceedingly presumptuous when one comes to think about it! Am *I* so central to the universe that *my* experience must fix the reality of a past and a future? Is the time of Julius Caesar now gone because *I* do not happen to share it? Is the Kingdom of Heaven not here because *I* am not yet ready for it? This ability to annul time does not extend to my capability with regard to space (or does Quantum theory suggest that perhaps it might?). I may be tempted to ignore the space which does not impinge directly upon me, but I am not so presumptuous as to deny its present reality. I am forced to admit that the mountain which is beyond my ken is no less real, no less presentable, than the hill which I happen to be climbing. If time and space are correlative what is the real situation here, and how can this disintegration of time into a past that is gone and a future that has not yet arrived be rationalized?

The implications of all this are staggering — especially for the concept of causality. Causality, as we usually think of it, implies an order of temporal precedence, but if the sequences of time should be altered or reversed or transcended would not different possibilities then present themselves in the way of causality. The late Arthur Koestler wrote:

> If time is treated in modern physics as a dimension almost on a par with the dimension of space, why should we *a priori* exclude the possibility that we are pulled as well as pushed along its axis? The future has, after all, as much or as little reality as the past, and there is nothing logically inconceivable in introducing as a working hypothesis an element of finality, supplementary to the element of causality into our equations.[4]

With similar logic psychologist Carl Jung put forward a radical proposal to the behaviourists of his day who assumed that the only factors affecting the subconscious were the experiences of the hidden past:

> The assumption that the human psyche possesses layers that lie *below* consciousness is not likely to arouse serious opposition. But that there could be just as well layers *above* consciousness seems to be a surmise which borders on a **crimen laesae majestatis humanae**. In my experience the conscious mind can only claim a relatively central position, and must put up with the fact that the

unconscious psyche transcends and as it were surrounds us on all sides. Unconscious contents connect it *backward* with psychological states on the one hand and archetypal data on the other. But it is extended *forward* by intuitions which are conditioned partly by archetypes and partly by subliminal perceptions depending on the relativity of time and space in the unconscious.[5]

It may be that a few generations "hence" the presently-held linear view of time will be considered as outmoded scientifically as the Ptolemaic earth-centred view of the heavens. Human creatureliness, of course, will still impose upon experience the three dimensional impression of time as belonging to past, present, and future just as it still imposes upon experience a stationary earth and the impression of space as consisting of length, breadth, and height. But realistically man will know better. He will realize that his old understanding of time as CHRONOS — time cut open and laid out like blocks on a calendar or divisions on a clock, or measurements in light years — has to submit to the more subtle but more realistic appreciation of time as KAIROS — "end time" which enlists temporality in a unity of being that is all-embracing.

No illustration is adequate at this point, but a homely one may be used provided that the analogy is not pressed. Man's place in life may be likened to the experience of a passenger seated in a motionless train who gains the feeling of forward movement when coaches on a track adjacent are backing up. So man stationed existentially gains the impression of progress from the relationship to him of life's impinging events. What has happened is that reality has exposed itself to him where he is and has forced relationships upon him which, experientially, create history. In that responsible moment man's involvement makes him an active participant in the shaped reality of life. He perceives *in situ* the profundity of the moment to which his being relates.

Fifty years ago when the evolutionary view of history was at its prestigious apogee Nicholas Berdyaev, the exiled Russian historian-philosopher, wrote:

The faith and trust which raise us above the present moment into the dimension of a great historical destiny should inspire us to do away once and for all with the disintegration of time into present, past and future, and set up the true era of eternity. Our belief and expectations should tend towards a solution in eternity of human destiny, towards a perspective of life based not on a detached future but on the eternal and integral present... Our function at every period is to determine our relation to our problem of life and history in the terms and according to the criterion of eternity. Only when we have situated human destiny and history in the perspective of eternity will the future appear no less real than the past, and the present no more real than either. The realization of a disintegrated time undertaken by the religion of progress is a sin before eternity.[6]

The question, of course, is how and where this "solution in eternity of human destiny" is to be found. There is no way whereby man himself can bridge the conceptual gulf which separates his time from eternity. Neither experimental science nor speculative thought can leap over that chasm. At this juncture natural sources are dependent upon revelation. *This* is the concern which Christian theology today might profitably address. Fortunately the theologian has biblical resources to inform him. Let me turn, therefore, from the scientific and philosophical considerations which have assumed such enigmatic interest to a brief review of the biblical witness to the mystery of the relationship of time and eternity.

This is not a simple or easy consideration. Certainly it is not simply a matter of quoting chapter and verse from "what the Bible says". The difficulty is that the idea of linear progression has so thoroughly permeated western thought as to obscure the perspective which is needed for a proper overview of the biblical witness to the divine disclosure. T. F. Torrance refers to "the kind of exegesis which detaches the phenomenal surface of the biblical narratives from the natural coherences in which they are rooted, so that the ontological import of the narratives and of their evidential grounds is destroyed."[7] For most people today, even for Christians, the Bible is no longer seen as witnessing to an action which, being the Word of

God, creates the reality to which the record bears witness. The Bible is seen, rather, as a kind of conglomerate record, inspired or otherwise, of a temporal development of religious thought which, with varying degrees of insight, reaches its apex, for the Christian believer at least, in the person and work of Jesus Christ.

This is not quite the way the Scriptures were meant to be understood. Those who transmitted the Bible never thought of it as the depository of a developing religious consciousness. They thought of it as a unified witness to the Word and Act of the God who had called men, in the varied conditions of their creatureliness, to relate to the purposes of his timeless will. Time and circumstance did not fix the revelation. The revelation addressed the circumstances which themselves were under the determination of God. The importance of the moment, accordingly, lay not in its being more "real" than the past or the future, nor did it lie in some antecedent preparation which it might be making, hopefully or fearfully, for the future. Its significance lay in the fact that it was the locale of eternity's impingement: "Today, if ye will hear his voice!". The writer of the apocryphal book of Judith declares: "Your hand has guided all that happened then, and all that happened before and after. You have planned it all — what is happening now, and what is yet to be. Your plans have always been carried out. Whatever you want to be done is as good as done. You know in advance all that you will do and what decisions you will make" (9.5–6, *Good News Bible*). In the Book of Ecclesiastes the writer stresses that man cannot escape his existence in time. "There is a time to be born, and a time to die; a time to plant, and a time to pluck up; a time to destroy and a time to heal" (3.2,3). God's sempiternity, however, is in no way restricted or conditioned by space/time circumstance. "Whatever God does endures for ever; nothing can be added to it, nor anything taken from it: ... That which is already has been; and God seeks what has been driven away" (3.15). The Old Testament prophets are for ever reminding the people that the purpose of history is to underline this fact. Isaiah reminds King Hezekiah that monarchs and men are but the instruments of Yahweh's will, and that the only real option before the nation when confronted by the seeming omnipotence of Sennacherib is to go on serving the Lord. "Have you not heard long ago? I did it. In days gone by I planned it. And now I have brought it about, making fortified cities tumble into heaps of ruin" (2 Chronicles 32).

Without this recognition of the sempiternity of God's Word, which is also God's Act, it is not possible fully to appreciate the central place which Jesus Christ has in the biblical revelation. To say that Jesus Christ is the locus of God's Word and Act is to acknowledge that it is the *Eternal* who has entered history. "My father works hitherto and I work." In order to deal adequately with the historical Jesus we have to admit within the hermeneutic of history the mystery of the word made flesh, embracing, as it does, the role of him "who is before all things and in whom all things hold together" (Colossians 1.17). "He is the image of the invisible God, the first born of every creature, for by him all things were created, and by him all things exist" (v. 16). The events which constitute the biblical revelation, accordingly, are not so much represented as belonging "before" or "after" Jesus Christ as being "type" or "anti-type" of Jesus Christ. Whether men happen to have lived before or after the year 31 A.D., their faith and unbelief are always being exercised in relation to him who is the alpha and the omega of life.

This identification of Jesus Christ with every member of humanity and the unity of his being in the eternal rule and reign of God introduces a wholly new factor into the human situation. Man no longer stands under the temporal determination of sin and death. He stands in the fellowship and under the eternal lordship of Jesus Christ who has successfully challenged sin and death. The New Testament presses to full and logical conclusions the implications of this achievement for the believer who is "incorporate" in Christ. Man's destiny is not fixed to a temporal order which has the seal of death upon it. His destiny is determined by the relationship in which he stands to Jesus Christ who is Lord of life and conqueror of death. "If any man be in Christ Jesus he is a new creation; old things are passed away; behold, all things are become new" (2 Corinthians 5.7).

Karl Barth in a moving paragraph in *Church Dogmatics*, where he is writing on "The Definiteness of the Divine Decision", says that, "Time does not continue after the death and resurrection of Jesus Christ. It can only move from this its centre to its divinely-appointed end. For its end is determined by the fact that it has been given this centre". Barth adds that, "the only question now is whether the Church will live or not live in the fulness granted to it, in recognition or non-recognition, in face of what God finally and once-for-all accomplished for man."

I am aware that such a Christ-centred view of history is incompatible with the linear-evolutionary view of history which has dominated western thought for the past two hundred years, but my contention is that this popular view must be challenged, and challenged now, not simply in the name of the Christian faith, but in the name of science itself. Since it is not within the province or the ability of natural science to establish a "criterion of eternity", I am not suggesting that biologists, physicists and cosmologists should now leap on the bandwagon of Pauline theology — hardly a pressing temptation at the present time! What I would urge, and urge emphatically, is that the Christian Church itself should so order its emphases as to give priority and true relevance to a Gospel of liberation. Nothing can be of more practical and immediate importance to the world than a rediscovery of the resources of grace which enable man, captive as he appears to be to an order which is subjected to futility, to transcend his creatureliness.

NOTES

1. Paul Davies, *op. cit.*, p. 119.
2. Davies, *ibid.*, p. 39.
3. Sir Fred Hoyle, *The Intelligent Universe*, p. 212.

4. Arthur Koestler, *The Sleepwalkers* (Hutchinson, London), p. 537.
5. C. G. Jung, *Collected Works*, vol. 12, *Psychology and Alchemy* (Pantheon Books, New York, 1953), p. 33.
6. Nicholas Berdyaev, *The Meaning of History* (The Century Press, London, 1945), pp. 195–6.
7. T. F. Torrance, *Space, Time and Resurrection* (Handsel Press, Edinburgh, 1976), p. 24.

CHAPTER 8

THE UNIQUENESS OF MAN

ONE of the momentous developments in modern science is the recognition that the apprehension of physical reality involves "the personal coefficient of knowledge". It is man who observes and apprehends, and without his involvement the secrets of nature fail to disclose themselves in a meaningful way. In chapter II I underlined the fact that it is impossible to separate man and nature, and that science in its study of nature has to take that fact into account.

Respect for this human ingredient in understanding has not generally characterized the work of modern science. On the contrary natural science has generally assumed that the first essential requirement of its work is objectivity on the part of the observer, that the person who is doing the observing must exclude himself from the facts he is observing. While this attitude of cool detachment is necessary for fact-finding in research it nevertheless distorts the relationship in which man stands to nature; when the scientist moves beyond the study of isolated phenomena to try to ascertain the nature of ultimate reality he finds himself integrated in it, his own being qualifying some of the relationships of the study he is making.

It was quantum behaviour which brought this awareness of observer involvement to the fore. The picture of the particle which emerged from Max Planck's study of black body radiation in the year 1900 resolved itself in a mental image the ingredients of which were seen to be constructs which existed and moved in conceptual space. It was no longer possible to "locate" the particle in the traditional space and time which was thought to exist independent of the observer. "If we insist on picturing (the particle) as a point", wrote Sir James Jeans, "then the relative intensities of the waves indicate the relative proprieties of supposing it to exist at the various points of space. Proprieties relative to what? The answer is: Relative to our knowledge."[1] The seeming contradiction between the wave picture and the particle picture was removed only when it was recognized that these images or patterns are not properties of light itself, but of the interaction of the investigator with light.

One reason science took so long to come to terms with quantum mechanics was because of this strange situation with regard to the observer role. These implications are now reverberating through the world of the intellect, and scientists themselves, even to a greater extent, perhaps, than theologians and philosophers, are trying to make the needed epistemic adjustments. John Wheeler, the eminent American physicist, asks:

> May the universe in some strange sense be "brought into being" by the participation of those who participate? ... "Participator" is the incontrovertible new conception given by quantum mechanics. It strikes down the term of "observer" of classical theory, the man who stands safely behind the thick glass wall and watches what goes on without taking part. It can't be done, quantum mechanics says.[2]

In fairness to Wheeler I would add that he himself is exceedingly cautious about the philosophical implications to be drawn from observer involvement. "Let us not invoke consciousness", he says, "as a pre-requisite for what in quantum mechanics we call the elementary act of observation." He appears to agree with Niels Bohr that, "Any device (human or otherwise) that indelibly records a quantum phenomenon counts as an observer".[3] This qualification, however, raises the question of whether "any device" other than a person does any observing. To record is not to observe. John Locke has said that, "It is impossible for any person to perceive without perceiving that he does perceive". But this is an aside. Regardless of how the observer role is interpreted the fact remains that physics has been forced to abandon the dualism which assumed that physical reality was something standing "out there" from which the scientist could stand impartially removed. The amazing co-relation of the physical universe with man, and the puzzling relationship in which man stands to the physical reality which engages him qualifies the scientific enterprise, and fixes in advance certain conditions of the scientific quest.

Quantum discovery has quickened science to the recognition of other aspects of human involvement in nature. One of the most interesting and controversial of these is the anthropic cosmological principle, so-called, which maintains that the circumstances and conditions which have led to the creation and development of the known world and universe are pre-requisites of the existence of observers and presuppose their eventual emergence. The evidence which is being used to support this remarkable theory is certainly incontrovertible; it is the interpretation of the evidence that is highly debatable. Let me take a brief look at some of the details.

The universe must be about ten billion light years in diameter because a smaller universe would have existed for less than the time required for human life to be synthesized by nuclear reactions in the interior of stars. If the universe were much bigger and hence much older, the stars needed to establish the conditions of life would have long since completed their evolution and burned out. The anthropic principle also bears on the universe's entropy level of 10 to 8. If this number were increased marginally it would not be possible for protogalaxies to condense to the density at which stars could form. But without the stars the solar system and the heavy elements of the living matter of life would not have been created. If the universe were initially fairly regular it would irreversibly have generated copious quantities of heat radiation because of the entropy-generating channels open to it at the time of the singularity. Again this would have resulted in an entropy and a radiation pressure far in excess of the values favouring the condensation of protogalaxies. Such a universe could not have been observed by man.

Turning from these cosmic considerations to sub-atomic constants of nature again we find pre-determining factors at work. As small an increase as 2 per cent would have blocked the formation of protons out of quarks and hence the formation of hydrogen atoms. A comparable decrease would have made nuclei that are essential to life unstable. Such minute chemical changes would have ruled out the existence of plant-supporting stars.

One could go on and on! It all adds up to the fact that the only universe man could know is the one that he does know, and that if certain constants of nature had been shifted, ever so slightly, another kind of universe would have evolved which would be scientifically inconceivable. Whether such universes exist we shall never know. In brief, *the conditions fixed at creation* with regard alike to the structure of the universe and the constitution of the matter comprising it *have a human limitation placed upon them.*

(Let me enter a caveat here concerning the ease with which writers of popular science today propose natural explanations of that for which the knowable laws of physics can provide no explanation. Conjectures about "reversed time causality" at work in "multiple universes" are now being made to try to explain scientifically how being came into being. These conjectures, more bizarre and exotic than anything that theologians ever devised in the most credulous of times, suggest that in these hypothetical regions "anything" could happen — any-thing, that is, except God speaking his Word. The reason I have ignored these conjectures is because they further complicate the riddle of the universe. It seems to me that the physicist who realizes that he must now shave in the dark should use Occam's razor, that is to say, he should seek the simpler rather than the most complex explana-tion. In the case of missing matter would not the mystery be less obscure if astrophysicists were to work from the premise that being brings matter into existence rather than that matter creates being? With matter in the state it is why do physicists go on assuming that it has to explain everything? Is not the biblical observation that "God who gives life to the dead and calls into existence the things that do not exist" just as explanatory as these last-resort conjectures?)

At the present time most scientists are sceptical, some contemptuous of the anthropic principle. They maintain that these variables appear remarkable only because this is the way things have turned out, and that one should not argue from what is back to what had to be. Others are not quite so sure. Although most scientists feel acutely uncomfortable with anything that smacks of a personalistic approach to things physical, certain astrophysicists now maintain that the "laws" of nature are so designed that man with his capability to observe and comprehend the universe was bound to emerge. It wasn't simply a case of natural evolution bringing this about. The being of man reflects and presupposes the kind of natural development from which the being of man had to emerge. Dr. Glen W. Schaefer who has had a distinguished career in mathematical physics and biology has said:

> The anthropic principle has arisen from the uneasiness felt by leading theorists over the extremely remote possibility that evolution, as understood, could have produced the known universe and man out of the large number of alternative universes. The term "anthropic" suggests to me that consciousness was first and not last, that in some sense the universe is reflecting the human mind — and yet the human mind is reflecting the universe. It is a very uneasy situation that is developing.[4]

Along a similar line Paul Davies has recently written: "The conventional position is that intelligence only arises as the end product of a long sequence of evolutionary changes which successively increase the degree of organization of matter. In short, matter first, mind later. But is this inevitably so? Could mind be the more primitive entity?"[5] After raising this question Davies goes on to make a statement which is all the more remarkable in view of his determined effort to keep every traditional conception of God out of the cosmic picture:

According to some physicists at least, the mind has a special status in regard to the quantum factor. If mind can "load the quantum dice" then a universal mind could, in principle, control everything that happens by directing the behaviour of every electron, every proton, every photon, and so on. Such an organizing power would escape our attention when we observe microscopic matter because the antics of any particular particle would still appear to be completely random. It is only in the collective behaviour of vast numbers of atoms that organization would be apparent, and we should proclaim the system to be mysteriously self-organizing. Such a picture of God might well be enough to satisfy most believers.[6]

A further consideration upon which I shall enlarge in chapter IX is not unrelated to this anthropic discussion, and I do not consider it debatable. The human capabilities, however they may have come about, are, as we shall see, of a transcendent quality and possess a moral significance which does not attach to the order which may be claimed to have produced and conditioned them. Blaise Pascal remarked that the dropping of a child's tear has more worth than all the movement of the milky way. The universe which produced the milky way is the universe which had to produce also the child's tear, but there is no moral comparison here. It is the being of man and not the discoveries of the telescope which decides the significance to be attached to creation.

Is it mere coincidence — and this kind of coincidence has nothing "mere" about it — that the observer appears to be an indispensable part of both the microphysical world and the macroscopic universe which he observes? If a time relationship is going to be introduced into this situation would it not appear that the end in view, namely the being of man, has fixed the beginning of all things, and that a purposive process is at work which predetermines the events that follow? Schaefer writes: "It seems to me that the whole thing is backwards, and that we have — in some way completely mysterious at the moment — developed evolution rather than that evolution has developed us."[7]

I know that many scientists, biologists in particular, refuse to entertain this kind of conceptual hypothesis. Jacques Monod, for example, argues in his book *Chance and Necessity* that the molecular process by which genetic information passes from DNA molecule to messenger RNA to protein macromolecules indicates that the creative activity precedes the development and that what seems like purpose or teleonomy is "merely" sequential. Purpose, he says, is the result rather than the cause of chance action.

> The ancient covenant (between man and nature) is in pieces; man knows at last that he is alone in the universe's unfeeling immensity, out of which he emerged only by chance. No more than his destiny is his duty anywhere ordained. It is to him to choose between the kingdom and the shadows.

Is there not a series of glaring contradictions in Monod's literary flight? Do blueprints come about by meaningless chance? From the fact that the blueprint comes first does one logically argue that what follows is meaningless chance? If man's duty belongs to an unfeeling immensity why should he bother to choose between the kingdom and the darkness? The spectacle of an eminent biologist arguing moral responsibility on such premises presents an interesting psychological study. Arthur Koestler sarcastically likened *Chance and Necessity* to Custer's Last Stand.

Monod's conclusion illustrates a remarkable and distressing phenomenon which is all too prevalent in the intellectual disciplines. I refer to the unrelatedness of the branches of studies which allows specialists in one area to pursue their work in seeming ignorance of the implications for their work of significant developments elsewhere. The psychologist Harold Morowitz has observed that:

> What has happened is that biologists, who once postulated a privileged role for the human mind in nature's hierarchy, have been moving relentlessly toward a hard-core materialism that character-

ized nineteenth century physics. At the same time, physicists, faced with compelling experimental evidence, have been moving away from strictly mechanical models of the universe to a view that sees the mind as playing an integral role in all physical events. It is as if the two disciplines were on fast-moving trains, going in opposite directions and not noticing what is happening across the tracks.[8]

The biologists are not the only scholars in this dilemma. On what track or siding are many of the present-day theologians? In recent years many of them, in an attempt to render theology credible to a secular society which is gasping for oxygen, have rejected the classical teleological and cosmological arguments for the existence of God. I find it ironic that physicists and cosmologists now discover these arguments presenting themselves at the front door of the house of science for admission. Not all scientists are slamming the door in their face. Science is more open to a straightforward theistic explanation of life and the universe than it has been for two centuries. There are those who contend that the reason the universe appears to be tailor-made for human existence is that God made it that way. One such physicist, Dr. Arno A. Penzias who shared with Robert W. Wilson the Nobel Prize for the discovery of evidence supporting the Big Bang theory of the origin of the universe, has confessed:

> What we find when we look at the universe is order... We also find direction. The universe has a very well-marked beginning. It starts with a creation — a big bang if you will — and has a directionality to it. We have a result for which there ought to have been a cause. And although there's no picture of an old man with a white beard standing there, what we see of the world from a physical point of view is consistent with what Maimonides observed from a metaphysical point of view — without a large telescope or watching the flight of the galaxies.[9]

NOTES

1 Sir James Jeans, *Physics and Reality*. The citation is from "The Second Argument for Mentalism" in the section "Some Problems of Philosophy" (Random House, New York, 1947), p. 393.

2. J. A. Wheeler, K. S. Thorne and C. Misner, *Gravitation* (Freeman, San Francisco), p. 1273.
3. *Scientific Digest*, October, 1984, p. 96.
4. Quoted from an interview in *The Christian Science Monitor*, July 12, 1979.
5. Paul Davies, *op. cit*, p. 210.
6. *Ibid.*, p.210–1.
7. *The Christian Science Monitor*, July 12, 1979.
8. H. Morowitz, "Rediscovering the Mind", *The Mind's I* (Harvester/Basic Books, 1981).
9. "American Jews Rediscover Orthodoxy", by Natalie Gittelson, *New York Times Literary Supplement*, Sept. 30, 1985, p. 64.

CHAPTER 9

THE TRANSCENDENT SELF

I looked at the manner in which the physical reality of the world and the universe relates itself to the being of man — the remarkable relationship which exists between nature and man. Let me now look at the other side of this relationship — the manner in which man, now he is here, relates to that reality of which he is seen to be an integral part. The remarkable thing here is that although the physical universe appears to have been made for man, man has obviously been made for more than the physical universe.

The distinctive thing about man, and the thing which renders him unique in the created order is a self-awareness which gives him a unique and even determining role in nature. The fact that man is able to look critically at himself and to view objectively the reality around him, even to the point of exercising a certain dominion over it, means that he stands outside and above his creatureliness. He is more than nature.

In considering this transcendence of the self we must, of course, distinguish between those physical neurological mechanisms and processes which are subject to nature's laws and conditions and the noetic activity of the brain which requires a different kind of evaluation. The human brain is a physical organ — not a simple one — functioning according to knowable laws of biochemistry and physics; but what goes on in the brain cannot be explained in terms of any known mechanical, chemical or physical laws. Man in his inner spirit is always transcending the rules and requirements which nature imposes on creation. Usually he is defying them. Let me illustrate.

The human mind or spirit does not obey the physical

laws of the conservation of energy; when nature gives up something a loss results, but when the mind gives up its thoughts it still keeps them.

The human mind or spirit does not obey the law of entropy; in the world of physics order naturally gives way to disorder, but the mind of man engages itself constantly in conceptual organization.

The human mind or spirit does not obey the basic law of energy which requires that nothing shall exceed the speed of light. $E = mc^2$. But man in the endless and timeless ranges of his thought constantly performs this impossible feat. It takes him neither more nor less time to conceive or image a star a million light years away than it takes to conceive or image a lamp on the desk nearby. In like fashion human thinking can project itself as readily to an imagined future as to a fulfilled past. Interesting and revealing in this regard are the images of the dream world in which the human mind or spirit, undisciplined by reason and logic, is able, momentarily, to experience events which in "real" life would require extensive time and vast space for their realization. The fact that in the dream world the mind is subjected to an "abnormal" state of consciousness does not invalidate this remarkable fact. The mind or spirit of man, whether in normal or in abnormal states, is able to "break the rules" which govern all spatial and temporal relationships. The space/time continuum which enables man to function existentially in the physical order finds its "universal" laws and regulations challenged by the human spirit.

In chapter VII I pointed out that the mind of man exercises dominion over time, consigning temporality to a past or a future of its own making. And now quantum behaviour raises the tantalizing possibility that particle elements of matter may likewise be subject to a kind of human determination.

This ability of man in the ranges of his thought to transcend the natural order has far-reaching implications for epistemology and for science. Just how realistic is it to claim universality and finality for laws which fail to apply to the most important part of creation — the spirit of man himself? The goal of science is to shed whatever light it can upon the reality which is open to every aspect of being. If science in the pursuit of this goal finds that man himself stands in a unique relationship to a universe which his spirit can transcend must not this fact be taken into account? Over half a century ago Sir Arthur Eddington wrote:

> Those who in the search for truth start from consciousness as a seat of self-knowledge with interests and responsibilities not confined to the material plane, are just as much facing the hard facts of experience as those who start from consciousness as a device for reading the indications of spectroscopes and micrometers.[1]

It is interesting to see how modern secular thought has tried to come to terms with this noematic situation. A religious age would never have tried to rationalize or scientize this capability of man to transcend himself and his world. It would have seen in this capability evidence that man, spiritually endowed and made in the image of God, is called to relate to a reality higher than that of the natural order. The presuppositions of modern thought, however, make no provision for such an endowment or the existence of such an order, and require that the method of rational investigation, the scientific method, be applied to every area of interest, including the human mind or psyche. This has presented modern science with something of a dilemma. Science can be an exact exercise in areas like physics, chemistry, cosmology, even biology up to the point where the human element does not impinge. But in areas like anthropology, sociology and history where, from the outset, the being of man must be taken into account, it is impossible to establish exactitude. How does one scientize the psyche? How does one meld an understanding of human life and being with the concepts which science uses to establish facticity? What has been attempted is a logic or science of the psyche, the psychological method, so-called, to try to explain rationally and scientifically those activities and relationships of the mind and spirit which defy rational scientific explanation.

The results of this attempt have proved less than convincing. The exact sciences have never quite known what to make of psychology and the studies which are related to it — sociology, anthropology, social science, political science et cetera. Recognition of the limitations of science in these areas is seen today in the scathing indictments of psychology, psychiatry and sociology which have now become fashionable in the very circles which hitherto gave them prestigious intellectual support. The eminent British critic George Conquest in an interview some time ago with an American correspondent said:

> My concern, as I look over your academy and mine, is the great flaw in our cultures, the alleged intellectualism, that is, thinking that one has a proven-scientific, guaranteed theory for every problem, whether military or social reform. Everybody seems to have blueprints, even in fields where no accuracy is attainable.
>
> When you see the Pentagon computerizing war, it's the same as the radical academic view for solving political problems. Modern educational theory is ninety percent drivel, modern literary criticism *is* drivel, and psychology is *not* a sound science after all.
>
> What is needed in our countries is much more intellectual modesty... There are no answers to everything.[2]

George Conquest may have overstated the case but his main point is valid. It is doubtful whether clear-cut relationships can be established outside the factual specializations; when it comes to understanding and trying to explain the behaviour of the human mind and spirit it would seem that science has no alternative but to acknowledge a realm of being which science cannot explain but must respect. Unless the scientist adopts an arbitrary dualism here, assigning to science the factual aspects of life and to metaphysics the things that belong to the mind and the spirit, he has the obligation to press for working relationships. Particularly if, as increasingly appears to be the case, it is from his own material discoveries that he has been brought to the threshold of a metaphysical awareness.

In any case, epistemology abhors a vacuum, and the failure of modern science to relate itself to dimensions of transcendence which the human spirit possesses has not left the field of knowledge void of speculation. The modern crisis of faith and the nihilism which accompanies it have stimulated increasing interest in philosophico-religious points of view which emphasize the uniqueness of man and the independence of the human spirit. Scholars who are sympathetic to eastern thought and pantheistic world views in particular are having something of a field day in this controversial area of speculation. Asserting that the structure and behaviour of the universe appear to have much in common with the human mind they claim support in the new physics for a kind of mentalism which rests simply upon the subjective awareness of reality. One thinks, for example, of the stimulating writings of Fritjov Capra in this regard. Sometimes the claim for mental autonomy assumes such a dominant form as to deny the being of any reality independent of that of the human mind or spirit. Thus Gary Zukav in his book, *The Dancing Wu Li Masters* has managed, by joining some major assumptions with a few non sequiturs to call in question the very existence of light itself:

> Since particle-like and wave-length behaviour are the only properties that we ascribe to light, and since these properties are now recognized to belong (if complementarity is correct) not to light itself, but to our interaction with light, then it appears that light has no properties independent of us! To say that something has no properties is the same as saying that it does not exist. The next step in this logic is inescapable. Without us, light does not exist.[3]

This seems like a high price to pay to get rid of materialism and one cannot help but feel that a healthy scepticism is needed when confronted with the claims of a subjectivistic philosophy which, at the end of the day, would prove destructive of the whole scientific enterprise. Perhaps, it is not surprising that an empirical science never came to any kind of full expression in lands of Buddhist and Taoist sympathies.

Recognition that the human mind or spirit exercises an independence of nature and a dominance over physical law does not imply a denial of nature's own reality and, as I shall point out in the next chapter, it certainly does not imply an ultimate autonomy on the part of man himself.

NOTES

1. Sir Arthur Eddington, *The World's Great Thinkers* (Random House, New York, 1947), p. 426.
2. Interview with Arnold Reichman in *The Christian Science Monitor*, May 20, 1971.
3. Gary Zukav, *The Dancing Wu Li Masters* (William Morrow, New York, 1979), p. 118.

CHAPTER 10

FAITH'S REALIZING LIGHT

IN the last chapter I spoke of the unique place which man occupies in the created order. The human mind or spirit transcends nature. Man cannot be explained by the material circumstances which condition the physical realities of his life. The writer of Psalm 8 sums up the situation realistically when he says that God "has crowned him (man) with glory and honour. Thou madest him to have dominion over the work of thy hands. Thou hast put all things under his feet." This uniqueness of man and the independence of his spirit are factors which science must take into account when trying to assess man's place vis-à-vis nature.

But here we face a paradox. And a supreme irony! Man, despite the moral supremacy of his place in nature finds a limitation placed upon him which renders him incapable of assuming the Promethean role entrusted to him. He remains in total ignorance both of himself and of the universe which he transcends. Alongside the Psalmist's assertion of "dominion over all things" we have the sober reminder of Ecclesiastes 3.11: "God has put eternity in his (man's) mind, yet ... he cannot find out what God has done from the beginning to the end."

I am aware that a blunt assertion of total ignorance on the part of man is not likely to go unchallenged, particularly in this accomplished day and age. A generation which has been able to put man on the moon and to unravel the genetic code can hardly be expected to confess total ignorance of life and being. The popular impression today is that the incredible knowledge now available to man and manipulated by him renders the secrets of the universe increasingly open to human understanding and control, and that ever less scope remains for a non-scientific view of life. Theology itself has tried to come to terms with this situation and holds in contempt the lingering conception of a "God of the gaps". Typical of this humanistic confidence is the observation of Professor Paul Davies in his book *God and the New Physics* to which I have already referred several times:

> Physics, the queen of sciences, has opened up vistas of human understanding that were unsuspected a few centuries ago. From the inner workings of the atom to the weird surrealism of the black hole, physics has enabled us to comprehend some of Nature's darkest secrets, and to gain control over many physical systems in the environment.[1]

On the strength of these material achievements Davies would now have science replace religion. "In my opinion," he wrote, "science offers a surer path to God than religion."

> By finding out more about the way the universe is put together and how it works, about the nature of life and consciousness, they (scientists) can supply the raw material from which religious beliefs may be fashioned... In many cases the old religious ideas are not so much disproved as transcended by modern science. By looking at the world from a different angle, scientists can provide fresh insights and new perspectives of Man and his place in the universe.[2]

Analyse this confidence and we find that the higher human knowledge which is to replace divine revelation belongs to the observable behaviour of matter as it finds sophisticated mathematical formulation. The "different angle", the "new perspective", is shot from the vantage point of signs and symbols which technology is invited to seize for the further control of human life and the conquest of the world's resources.

What grounds are there here, might I ask, for self-aggrandizement? The sobering fact remains that man still knows nothing about himself or about the universe of which he is the crowning glory. Not one of the "Night Questions" which man asked when he first gained self-awareness — "Who am I?", "Where did I come from?",

"Why am I here?", "Where am I going?" — is any closer
to rational solution than when first posed. As for that
factual knowledge which grows exponentially, is this not a
case of man knowing ever more about an ever-growing
mystery? The scientist's knowledge of "some of nature's
darkest secrets" does not extend to any real understanding of *what* matter is, or *why* it behaves the way it does, or
how it came to be. The mystery which surrounds matter
has only deepened since Sir Arthur Eddington concluded
that "no familiar conceptions can be woven around the
electron; it belongs to the waiting list... *something
unknown is doing we know not what.* That is what our
theory amounts to."[3] It is ironic that one of the most
sophisticated formulas of modern physics — the "uncertainty principle" to which Heisenberg has given mathematical precision (sic! mathematical precision to uncertainty!) shows that man's attempt to gain understanding
distorts the reality which he is seeking to understand, and
renders rational explanation of the behaviour of physical
matter impossible.

It is within this paradox — the awareness that man,
though crowned with glory and honour, nevertheless,
knows nothing that has been done from the beginning —
that science pursues its quest for understanding. The
pure scientist today is in the plight of Tintoretto, the
seascape artist, who, trying to capture on his canvas the
changing mood of the ocean, finally threw down his
brushes in despair and cried: "It keeps growing ever
larger!". The Psalmist's observation still holds: "When I
look at thy heavens, the work of thy fingers, the moon and
the stars which thou hast established, what is man that
thou are mindful of him, and the son of man that thou
dost care for him?" (8. 3–4).

This human dilemma begs a theological observation:
the late Simone Weil remarked that, "Man merely exists,
only God is".[4] Weil hastened to remind the reader that
the verb "to exist" means to be "out of being". Man in his
creatureliness remains shut out of reality. "Now I know
in part." (I Corinthians 13. 12). His creatureliness

renders him incapable of bridging the gulf between the finite and the infinite. Any hope that man possesses of grasping the nature of ultimate reality resides in the possibility of illumination coming to him from beyond the scope of his rational understanding. It lies in revelation.

It is here that the uniqueness of man's place in the universe becomes apparent. The rest of creation is incapable of receiving truth concerning the things of God, but man, made in the divine image, has been granted a faith capability which renders belief operative. In the words of Feodor Dostoievsky's Russian monk, "Much on earth is hidden from us, but to make up for that we have been given a precious mystic sense of our living bond with the other world, and the roots of our thought and feeling are not here but in other worlds."[5]

The Christian, of course, has to be cautious here if his understanding of faith is to be true to the witness of Scripture. This faith capability is not to be thought of as some faculty of the inward self with its source in man's own spiritual endowment. The fact that it is inward does not mean that it is self-derived. Karl Barth has reminded us that:

> In faith it is not at all the case that on an irrational and supra-empirical interior level of human consciousness man arrives at a unity with God in the form of the suspension of the subject-object relationship of the limitation in which God is revealed to us. Nor is our faith, and with it our knowledge of God, fulfilled in such a way that deep down God's own knowing of himself is naturally inherent in our being and activity in faith.[6]

"The only proper ground of faith", as T. F. Torrance has said, "is the reality to which it is correlated as its objective pole."[7]

The biblical witness here is of very great importance, and I believe that it must be considered normative for the understanding of faith. According to the Bible the source of believing faith is the Word of God addressed to man who is endowed with the gift of attention, the capacity to hear. "Faith comes by hearing" (Romans 10. 17). The

understanding which this divine wisdom possesses transcends the reaches of human understanding. "The wisdom
that is from above is first pure, then peaceable, gentle,
open to reason, full of mercy and good fruits, without
uncertainty or insincerity" (James 3.17). Its logic is
contained within itself and provides the ultimate basis of
human understanding. The classic text is Hebrews 11.
1–3: "Now faith is the *substance* (literally the 'under-stand-
ing') of things hoped for, the *evidence* of things not seen."
Far from being a kind of gap-filler to be used pending the
arrival of certain knowledge, faith itself constitutes the
certain knowledge and its exercise makes real the
understanding that is being sought. The human response
to this disclosure of the Word, accordingly, is not rational
analysis but obedience. "Speak, Lord, for thy servant
hears" (I Samuel 3. 9). If the believer does not act he has
not heard.

The classic Old Testament illustration of faith is the
hearing and doing of Abraham, the father of the faithful.
It is interesting to recall that Abraham by temperament
was not a credulous person. He was the most realistic of
men, systematic in his thinking and ordered in his
behaviour. But his sense of reverence was finely tuned and
he exercised fully the faculty of attention. Thus when the
Word of the Lord came to him — and it is instructive to
note how critically he always received it — he had no
alternative but to obey, even when his obedience seemed
to vitiate the promise and render its fulfilment impossible.
His only response to Isaac's plaintive query re ways and
means had to be the heart-breaking rejoinder that "God
will provide himself a lamb for the burnt offering".

May I suggest that this biblical understanding of faith
as openness to a wisdom that is from above, the disclosure
of which hinges upon personal commitment, far from
being antithetical to the needs of science, constitutes a
basic requirement of science. For the scientist no less than
for the religious believer Anselm's dictum applies: *Credo
ut intelligam* ("I believe in order that I may understand").
Michael Polanyi has pointed out that all knowledge,

including the knowledge which experimental science regards as objective, is never isolated from knowers. It belongs to persons and is held by them. The idea of knowledge independent of the knower is as meaningless as the concept of a tool apart from its function. The basic requirement of understanding is respect, the recognition that, in Einstein's phrase (borrowed from Leibniz), "a pre-established harmony" exists between human thought and empirical reality and that when man ventures in "confidence", that is to say, "with faith", the universe responds. "He that cometh to God must believe that he is, and that he is the rewarder of them that diligently seek him."

Nowhere in the arena of science is this pre-established harmony more evident than in the enterprise of higher mathematics upon which pure science relies for its basic constructs. William G. Pollard has pointed out that four of the major mathematical systems developed since the 17th century (Newton's theory of gravity, Riemann's tensor analysis, the properties of Hilbert space, and the abstract algebra of Sophus Lie), which were produced "initially as pure products of the human mind" simply for the delight of their inner beauty, "turned out to mirror the workings of the natural world accurately and precisely in every detail in ways completely unforeseen and unexpected by their originators".[8] In reference to this he cites Eugene Wigner who said, "The miracle of the appropriateness of the language of mathematics for the formulation of the laws of physics is a wonderful gift which we neither understand nor deserve."[9]

Michael Polanyi has made the further observation that all the processes of what he calls "creative guesswork" in mathematical discovery have in common that they are guided by the urge to make contact with a reality which is felt to be already there to start with, waiting to be apprehended. "In this light," he says, "it may appear more appropriate to regard discovery in natural sciences as guided not so much by the potentiality of a scientific proposition as by an aspect of nature seeking realization in our minds."[10]

The story of modern theoretical science from James Clerk Maxwell through to Arthur Eddington, Albert Einstein and Max Planck is the story of respect for things unseen and reliance upon the faithfulness of a universe which is waiting to reward man in his humble search for truth. Without this confidence twentieth century science could never have rebuilt its edifice of physics following the disintegration of the classical footings — footings, incidentally, which made no provision for believing faith.

It is true, of course, that the scientist *qua* scientist, exercises faith and intuition in an area or field of interest which differentiates itself from the sphere of religious understanding. The natural scientist is not seeking to ascertain the will of God through the leading of the Holy Spirit — at least that is not his avowed intent; but all truth is the truth of God, and if the scientist is seeking truth in his particular sphere, and if there is a unity in nature he has the right to expect that a search for understanding made with integrity and humility will have its faith reward. If this pursuit of truth should bring him to a hiatus — as happened to the physicists in this century — he has the alternative of supposing that no further knowledge can be gained or of taking a leap of faith which is likely to land him in an unfamiliar place. If he is a "pure" scientist he takes the leap of faith; like Anselm, he believes in order that he may understand.

This recognition by science of faith as understanding is one of the more promising developments in what is otherwise a somewhat depressing epistemological scene, and its implications are likely to have hopeful consequences. When it comes to be generally recognized in intellectual circles that man has to believe in order to understand, and that it is faith that summons him to knowledge, it will become apparent that the dualism which has existed for too long between logic and intuition, mind and heart, reason and revelation, is no longer permissible. The consequences of this for both science and religion cannot help but be positive and rewarding.

NOTES

1. Paul Davies, *God and the New Physics*, pp. 5–6.
2. *Ibid.*, p. 3.
3. A. S. Eddington, *The Nature of the Physical World*, from the section on "The Definition of Reality", p. 426.
4. Simone Weil, *First and Last Note-Books* (Oxford University Press, London, 1970), p. 329.
5. Feodor Dostoievsky, *The Brothers Karamazov* (Random House, New York), pp. 384–5.
6. Karl Barth, *Church Dogmatics*, II.1, p. 57.
7. T. F. Torrance, *Space, Time and Resurrection*, p. 24.
8. William G. Pollard, "Rumors of Transcendence in Physics", *American Journal of Physics*, vol. 52 (10), October, 1984, p. 880.
9. *Ibid.*, p. 881.
10. Michael Polanyi, *Science, Faith and Society* (University of Chicago Press, 1964), p. 44.

CHAPTER 11

THE NATURE OF ULTIMATE REALITY

THE word "science" derives from the Latin word "to know" (*scire*). Its original reference was to universal knowledge, the scope of which embraced all specialties including philosophy and theology. Prior to the late seventeenth century the intellectual prestige of the Christian Faith gave the biblical revelation a place of paramount importance in theories of knowledge, and Christian theology was regarded as the queen of the sciences.

As long as respect continued to be held for the empirical data of the biblical revelation Christian theology retained its honoured and preeminent place in epistemology, but when, under the dominant influence of modern thought, science came to embrace the view that the only data acceptable to its studies were factual and quantifiable, open to experimental and mathematical description, the data of revelation became suspect and their content was increasingly regarded as irrelevant to the method and subject-matter of science. Thus separated alike from both speculative thought and revelation the science of the 18th and 19th centuries (this, in theory at least — actually the scientist cannot help but speculate!) acquired its present restricted meaning as knowledge derived from human observation and research. Karl Pearson in his *Grammar of Science* states that "the classification of facts and the formation of absolute judgments on the basis of this classification — judgments independent of the idiosyncrasies of the individual mind — essentially sum up the aim and method of modern science."[1] This is the view of science which is popularly held today and it appears to be shared by most scientists themselves. Allan Sandage, the distinguished American astronomer, referring to his work at the Hale telescope in southern California recently said: "Even though I have been privileged to observe here for 24 years, every time I come into the dome I am terrified by the shape and significance of this instrument. *Here is where we find Absolute Reality*."[2]

In these pages I have contended that, insofar as the work of the pure or theoretical scientist is concerned, this popular conception of science does not quite correspond to the real situation. There is more at stake in the scientific enterprise than "the classification of facts". Belief or faith, as we have seen, has an essential part in the undertaking. To insist upon this is not to minimize the need for material exactitude in scientific work. Simone Weil (no mean mathematician herself) has said that

> We must suppose the rational in the Cartesian sense, that is to say, mechanical rule or necessity in its humanly demonstrable form, to be everywhere it is possible to suppose it, in order to bring to light that which lies outside its range... The uncomprehended hides the incomprehensible and should on this account be eliminated.[3]

Ironically the very discoveries and achievements of the 20th century which have rendered modern science so prestigious are forcing upon it a more catholic appreciation of its work and a more modest estimate of its role in understanding the nature of ultimate reality. In all fields of knowledge today there is a moving away from the abstract study of forms of nature to an exploration of inner relationships, an attempt to uncover the inner coherence and wholeness of being. Having taken nature apart and thoroughly analysed the parts, the aim now is to try to reassemble nature and see it whole. Science cannot isolate itself from this *Zeitgeist* or spirit of the age. Indeed, science is now contributing significantly to this task. Professor Torrance, writing on the basic change in the concept of reality which has overtaken physics in this century, speaks of " a dynamic view of the world, a

continuous integrated manifold of fields of force in which
relations between bodies are just as ontologically real as
the bodies themselves, for it is in their interrelations and
transformations that things are found to be what and as
and when they are."[4]

It is not surprising, therefore, to find that in physics,
the most sophisticated branch of natural science, the locus
of interest has shifted to the search for a unified field
theory, the manifestation of a single force which,
embracing the reality of space and time, energy and
matter, will explain all the disparate forces of the
universe. No one familiar with the scientific discoveries of
the 19th and 20th centuries will question the high degree
of complexity which lies on the physical side of nature's
reality. To find on the other side of this appalling
complexity a simple principle of coherence, a unity in
creation, gives science its ultimate challenge.

What must be recognized is that the discovery by
physics of a unified field theory will not solve the riddle of
the universe. At best it may do for physics what the
discovery of the DNA molecule has done for biology —
uncover some of the mechanisms involved in the fearfully
complex relationships of matter and being. Albert
Einstein who struggled for the last thirty years of his life
to discover a unified field theory, discussing with Chaim
Tschernovitz the nature of ultimate reality said: "We
know nothing about it at all. Our knowledge is but the
knowledge of school children... We shall know a little
more than we do now. But the real nature of things — that
we shall never know — never!"[5] In the world of physical
reality no major discovery is made which does not point to
a mystery beyond itself. Pascal wrote:

> Our soul is cast into the body where it finds number, time,
> dimensions; it reasons about these things and calls them natural or
> necessary, and can believe nothing else. Unity added to infinity does
> not increase it at all, any more than a foot added to an infinite
> measurement; the finite is annihilated in the presence of the infinite
> and becomes pure nothingness.[6]

This basic limitation of science is finding increasing recognition in intellectual circles today, and it is this awareness which marks the striking difference between the rather dogmatic self-assurance of science at the turn of the century and the humbler and more open attitude which exists today. I doubt whether many scientists today would dismiss as irrelevant to the understanding of nature those "extra-scientific perceptions" (if I might coin a phrase!) which are found, say, in the music of a Bach, the poetry of an Eliot or the painting of a Van Gogh. How could they when the very mathematics upon which they rely for conceptual formulation is so poetically and figuratively contrived? Interesting in this connection is an observation made recently by Carl Friedrich von Weizsäcker in his formidable book, *The Unity of Nature*. "Science in the modern sense", he says, "is the collective achievement of a social group." What he proposes — and Heisenberg seems to support the view — is not more sophisticated geometric theories, but ways of reconciling the dizzying range of existing ones. He suggests that an attempt be made to intermesh with quantum theory biological cybernetics, the Platonic theory of forms and any other profound concepts which, hopefully, can support and elucidate each other. "The realization of the unity of nature, if scientifically feasible, can only come as a result of this collective achievement."

It seems to me that when science comes to the point of admitting that it might profitably embrace "the collective achievement of a social group" in order to perceive the unity of nature, Christian theology has both the right and the duty to reassert the proven relevance to science of the revelation of the Christian faith. In chapter II I touched on the relationships which have existed historically between science and the Christian religion, suggesting that it was this historic revelation which inspired modern science and fixed the direction of its development. The biblical understanding that "God made the earth by his power, fixed the world in place by his wisdom, unfurled the skies by his understanding" (Job 26), implied the kind of order and cohesion at the heart of nature which science needed both to investigate and to pursue its work. The further New Testament emphasis that man, despite the fall, remains the image-bearer of God, transformingly remade in Jesus Christ, inspired modern man to exercise both his endowment of reason and his capacity for faith in the scientific quest. It is difficult to see how either the natural sciences or the social sciences could have come to anything like their modern expression outside this theological framework.

In view of this interaction it hardly seems realistic for the scientific community today, in its attempt to find unity in nature, to invoke a host of gap-fillers from realms of conjecture, while ignoring the specific content of the revelation which undergirds the enterprise and gives it its meaning. Robert W. Manweiler asks:

> If we accept as a tentative goal the search for unity should not this unity be one including both the creation and its receiving rational creatures? Since God created man and the cosmos together, should we not expect a complex interaction to exist between the perceiving subject and creation, which also must be reflected within an overall unifying perspective?[7]

That such interaction between God, man and things does exist is now suggested by some of the more recent discoveries of physical science itself, and by way of bringing this subject into sharper focus I should like to make a hurried overview of the scene which appears to be opening up on further horizons of natural science, particularly in the areas of paleontology, biology and organic chemistry. All of these and other vistas invite detailed study which goes beyond the scope of these pages and the competence of the writer, but the vistas are fascinating and must be further explored.

Some years ago the late Loren Eiseley, a paleontologist, commenting on the possible creation of life in the laboratory wrote:

> I do not think, if someone finally twists the key successfully in the tiniest and most humble house of life, that many of (the basic)

questions will be answered.... Rather, I would say that if 'dead' matter has reared up this curious landscape of fiddling crickets, song sparrows and wondering men, it must be plain to the most devoted materialist that the matter of which he speaks contains amazing, if not dreadful, powers, and may not impossibly be, as Hardy suggested, 'but one mask of many worn by the Great Face behind'.[8]

Since Loren Eiseley's time biology has uncovered more of the knowable physical and chemical forces behind the vital processes of life, and the "devoted materialist" still defends his materialism. But the wonder of life is now seen to lie not in these material forces themselves but in the amazing molecular base of their organization.

The amazement of molecular structure extends beyond organic life to inorganic matter. Ponderable evidence has accumulated that remarkable coherence and organization belong to the molecular structure even of lifeless matter so-called. If, by organic, we mean a capacity to respond to processed information, then *all* matter appears to be organic.

In the universe itself a vital energy appears to be at work which makes for wholeness and order. The argument from entropy has long been pressed, and I shall not labour it. According to the Second Law of Thermo-dynamics a fundamental property of matter is its tendency to increasing disorder. But a "counterforce", explained by physics as a coupling to gravity which opens the way for the injection of order into cosmic material by the gravitational field, prevents the disarray. (We note that our own insignificant planet has kept a steady temperature for the four billion years of its existence and appears, to the lay person, to be sustained by something that looks remarkably like an energy of good will.)

In fields of biology and organic chemistry the implica-tions of quantum mechanics are proving of startling consequence. While the physicists have been probing their quarks, neutron stars and black holes to find a unity in nature some of the world's leading biologists, resisting the bias of their profession, have been suggesting that mind itself may be integral to nature and that organic life can never be reduced to the mechanical motions of its charged particles. The late W. H. Thorpe, ethologist at the University of Cambridge, wrote in his book, *Purpose in a World of Change*, that if we try to understand the human mind with its freedom of will, "we will find the universe dissolving into an infinity of mind which is, can only be, the sole way of understanding the universe." He says that just as today's physicists have had to move beyond the idea of mechanism as the basis of the physical world, so biologists are coming to the point where "it is necessary to look once again at our knowledge of the sense organs, the brain, the mind, and the relations between these last two" as the key to understanding the reality underlying the natural world. In doing so, he says, molecular biology is likely to find its world of mechanical models superseded by more adequate images of reality.

At this stage of its understanding science is generally reluctant to ascribe consciousness to the molecular relationships of matter, whether the matter be organic or inorganic. Indeed it is more likely to react with horror to the suggestion that matter discloses purposeful will. Note, for example, the furore created recently in biological circles over Rupert Sheldrake's hypothesis of "Formative Causation". According to the Editorial of *Nature*, the prestigious scientific magazine, his book, *A New Science of Life*, was "the best candidate for burning there has been for many years."!) At this stage of the game scientists prefer to use question-begging words like "synchronicity" and "symbiosis" to describe the dynamic interplay of matter and energy in the universe. But whatever descriptive language is used science must acknowledge that all the physical constants — the ways that matter and energy relate — are tuned just right to keep this particular universe of which man himself is its most significant entity in existence.

In the sixth century B. C. Thales, the Greek philosopher, taught that all matter, including minerals and gases, is alive, and a century afterwards Anaxagoras propounded a panspermatic theory maintaining that a harmony exists between man and nature, mind and the universe. Physical science today, forced to abandon the lifeless materialism of the nineteenth century, stands close to some of these philosophic ideas of ancient times. James E. Horrigan writes:

> If we have learned anything in recent years, it is that there exists a complete harmony between man, his mind and conscious activity, and the environment on the whole. Through discoveries into the very nature of things, man has opened up an entire new spectrum to the picture of a well-designed world. We may now observe that the very intrinsic nature of things, in and of the environment, reveal a mutual reciprocity that goes exceedingly far beyond mere compatibility in the usual evolutionary sense of adaptation, as with other life forms. In whatever course or direction man's creative thought and ingenuity chooses to carry him, the world is a complementary and well-prepared "stage" for his uses and purposes in a truly progressive sense, having not yet been found wanting in the provision of a physical environment containing all the necessary elements, forces and conditions — severally and in combination — to the attainment of his ever-enlarging objectives. *The potential for this most meaningful and unique mind-matter relationship, it should be emphasized, was latent in the material substance, force, and other phenomena before the advent of man.*[9] (italics mine)

What emerges conceptually from all this? When biologists talk about the elementary attraction of friendly molecules, and physicists postulate a counterforce at work in the universe which prevents depletion of energy, and cosmologists say that the universe has to be viewed in terms of a dynamic unity in which all action and reality have a common focus, is not one drawn to the conclusion that there is an "Influence" at work behind the material phenomena which wills the coherence and order of all things that exist. When, further to this, the evidence suggests that man himself, far from being the accidental byproduct of chance evolution is the precondition of its change, does not the biblical declaration that creation is the work of God and man the bearer of his image force itself upon us?

NOTES

1. Karl Pearson, *Grammar of Science*, (Macmillan, New York, 1911), p. 11.
2. Quoted from the article, "The Once and Future Universe", in *The National Geographic Magazine*, Vol. 163, No. 6 — the underlining and capitals are his.
3. Simone Weil, *Gravity and Grace* (Routledge and Kegan Paul, London, 1972), p. 119.
4. T. F. Torrance, *Space, Time and Resurrection* (The Handsel Press, Edinburgh, 1976), p. 185.
5. Quoted by Gordon H. Clarke in *Horizons of Science* (Harper and Row, San Francisco 1977), p. 268.
6. Blaise Pascal, *Penseés*, Series II, 418.
7. Quoted by John E. Haas, Jr., in *JASA* (September, 1983), p. 146.
8. Loren Eiseley, "Over the Past Seventy-Five Years", *The Christian Science Monitor*, October 8, 1983.
9. James Horrigan, "The Key to Reconcile Modern Science and Religious Thought", *JASA*, December, 1983, pp. 214–5.

CHAPTER 12

GOSPEL TRUTH

MAX Planck summed up the basic limitation of
science when he said that, "Science cannot solve the
ultimate mystery of nature. And this is because, in the last
analysis, we ourselves are part of nature and therefore part
of the mystery that we are trying to solve."[1]

In the preceding chapter I mentioned that recognition
of this limitation has created an openness on the part of
science to the contribution it might profitably receive
from insights of philosophy and religion which are
outside its own specialties.

It must be recognized, however, that the plant of
science cannot be nurtured in just any kind of conceptual
soil and that there is an intellectual environment which is
not only unfavourable to its growth but fatal to its life.
The irony in the current situation is that the throne atop
the ivory tower which Christian theology has vacated now
finds claimants in popular religious and philosophical
ideas which could eventually prove destructive of science
itself. These views run the gamut from the sophisticated
idealism of a Teilhard de Chardin whose cosmic Christ is
a kind of Man-Writ-Large to the sweeping pantheism of
eastern cults in which Nature, Humanity and God are
virtually indistinguishable. At a superficial glance these
idealistic and pantheistic views of man and nature appear
to lounge comfortably in the house of modern science.
They reject the materialism of the 19th century, they
embrace the principle of indeterminacy which quantum
theory has uncovered; they share an intuitive approach to
understanding, and they underline the unique and
determining role which man himself occupies in nature.
But note where they emerge! Since God or the Absolute is

a rather vague entity whose pantheistic ways are past finding out man himself becomes the locus of reality, and the very dilemma to which Planck referred is exacerbated. It is left to man to justify the ways of God. The objectivity which natural science requires to make sense of its work is replaced by a subjectivity which is ultimately hostile to its enterprise. Obviously science is in trouble if this kind of subjectivity should ever come to prevail in epistemology. Michael Polanyi has reminded us that, "Any effort to understand something must be sustained by the belief that there is something there that can be understood."[2] A science deprived of objectivity would be without its raison d'être.

It is important to distinguish the manner in which the understanding of the Christian Gospel separates itself from all such philosophical and religious speculations. The distinctive thing about the Christian understanding is that it is anchored to empirical data or "givens" which are disclosed to man where he is actually situated. The ultimate source or ground of the disclosure, like the ultimate source of all that man can think or know, lies quite outside the frame of human comprehension, but, given to faith and appropriated in faith, it enters the mainstream of empirical reality with data challenging man to relationship and commitment. "With this ambiguous earth his dealings have been told us." The data of the Gospel thus provide metaphysics with a firm empirical base and give both reason and revelation a common field for exercise. T. F. Torrance writes:

> What our actual knowledge does tell us is that ultimate Truth meets us on this side of that chasm within our mundane experience, where it is accessible to us and amenable to our statements. Therefore we have to think theological Truth and think it out from its own real centre on this side where it has established itself.[3]

If this understanding of faith's disclosure is valid then Christian theology, far from isolating itself from the concerns of natural science, must assume a central interpretative role in the field.

Unfortunately there appears to be a reluctance on the part of the intellectual leadership of the Christian community to take up this challenge. Grateful that the past tensions which existed between science and religion have eased the community appears to be content to let bygones be bygones and to settle for a *modus operandi* of the two disciplines, leaving to science the things that belong to science and to God the things that belong to God. Underlying this accommodating attitude there may be the unconscious assumption that science has now demonstrated its competence to deal with the things of nature so convincingly that no scope remains in the realm of things material and physical for Christian input. What remains is for the Christian Faith to try to give science its moral incentive and the scientist his spiritual motivation. Thus Donald M. MacKay, a distinguished specialist in analogue computing and brain physiology who was also a devoted Christian, pointed out that, "The scientist tries, in principle to make his descriptions exhaustive in their own terms on their own level. But this doesn't in the least mean that he is trying to exclude or invalidate descriptions at other levels where meaning may in fact be more important."[4]

It seems to me that to settle for this, (to each his own), approach is to underestimate the basic limitation of science and thereby to render science a disservice. The fact is that science desperately needs the very thing that Gospel truth claims to possess — the incarnational evidence of reality. What is it, really, that science explains? Let me be presumptuous enough to say that it is not reality. If I might use a crude illustration, the scientific description of physical reality is to the reality itself what the printed menu of a meal is to the meal. Hopefully the printed menu corresponds descriptively to the composite make-up of the dishes that will eventually come out of the kitchen, but the menu can never constitute the meal, nor can it in any way re-present it. The mathematical description, in Torrance's words, "is not the equivalent of some ontic structure of reality".[5]

The pure scientist would be the first to recognize this. "What we observe", said Heisenberg, "is not nature itself, but nature exposed to our method of questioning". Ultimately it is faith which enables the believer to "taste and see". Karl Barth has written:

> There is a truth in itself, proper and permanent, valid and right as such, which can become the content and order of man's language and action. But this possibility is not an independent possibility which man himself can control. It is a possibility which is imparted to him by the speaking and acting of God. With him is the truth; it is his truth; he himself is the truth. If we know the truth it can happen only by the liberation which comes from the truth itself.[6]

Science today, faced with the realization that the known and the knowable laws of nature provide no explanation of the ultimate nature of reality has opened itself to "methods of questioning" which extend far beyond traditional kinds of scientific analysis. Forced by relativity theory at the turn of the century to combine with its three dimensions of space the fourth dimension of time, scientific inquiry is now, at the end of the same century, incorporating into its unified field postulates undreamed of a hundred years ago to serve the needs of quantum reality. The question I would raise is whether it is quite unrealistic to suggest that science might now embrace a crowning dimension of grace which will enable it to take into account the moral and spiritual realities of life and being?

No doubt I shall be reminded that such a proposal *is* unrealistic because it involves the attempt to integrate into the study of things that are finite a dimension of reality which is quite incommensurate with it. Did I not quote Pascal a few pages back about the finite being "annihilated in the presence of the infinite"? This reminder, I repeat, ignores the achievement of the incarnation: "God was in Christ reconciling the world to himself" (2 Corinthians 5. 19). (The poet-philosopher Goethe observed that, "the spirit tends to take to itself a body".) The distinctive thing about the Gospel and the recognition which renders Gospel truth unique, is the fact that Eternity *has* related himself to time, and Infinity *has* assumed apprehensible form. For the believer the work of God in grace can never quite be separated from the work of God in nature. In Barth's words "God is the being of all beings, the law of all laws, and therefore the nature of every nature."[7] In nature the physical counterpart of grace is the unity in creation which, beginning with God's control of the inconceivable element of the particle, extends to the uttermost reaches of the illimitable cosmos. Without this divine sustenance and support the whole created universe would disintegrate into what Karl Barth calls "nothingness" and the apostle Paul calls "futility". Were God ever to cease to give himself, that is to say, to love, all would be lost.

The logic of this Christian understanding of reality is inescapable. The believer who looks at life and the world and the universe *sub specie aeternitatis* has no alternative but to pray, and to pray without ceasing. "Why, even the hairs of your head are numbered. Fear not; you are of more value than many sparrows" (Matthew 12.7).

The Christian who believes this way and for whom faith is the substance of his hope will not expect the scientific community to embrace this understanding simply because he says so, or because the Bible says so, or because the community of faith says so. The tragic fact is that the Christian community itself is too compromised by the world to make a convincing argument for faith. What the believer can do is to invite science to put this Christian understanding to the heuristic test which science itself recognizes as essential for establishing the truth of evidence.

> O make but trial of his love;
> Experience will decide
> How blest are they, and only they
> Who in his truth confide.

The rationale for re-establishing relationship between science and the Gospel truth, I repeat, is now established by the necessities of science itself. We see now that science is not some remote construct to be placed upon a space/time framework for dispassionate measurement and study. The physical universe is alive and responsive in all its parts, and is waiting to disclose its meaning and purpose to the creature who was made in the image of the Creator, and is prepared to be the instrument of his will.

The Christian stands here in a privileged position. He knows that God has not left his fallen world without a witness. The way, the truth and the life have been disclosed to him in Jesus Christ, "the image of the invisible God" (Colossians 1. 15). This disclosure does not rest upon an intellectual paradigm which can be grasped only by those possessed of comprehensive factual knowledge and remarkable mental acumen. Resting upon faith which works through love it is available to all the sons of men, and it remains the hope of understanding for all who would comprehend, "what is the breadth, and length, and depth, and height ... and be filled with all the fulness of God" (Ephesians 3. 18–19).

NOTES

1. P. E. Hughes, *Christianity and the Problem of Origins* (Presbyterian and Reformed Publishing Company, Philadelphia, 1964), p. 37.
2. Michael Polanyi, *Science, Faith and Society* (University of Chicago Press, 1964), p. 44.
3. T. F. Torrance, *Theological Science* (Oxford University Press, London ,1969), pp. 45–6.
4. D. M. MacKay, "Brain Research and Human Responsibility", in Chapter IX of *Horizons of Science*.
5. T. F. Torrance, *God and Rationality* (Oxford University Press, London, 1971), p. 84.
6. *Church Dogmatics*, II.1, p. 208.
7. *Church Dogmatics*, II.1, p. 334.

INDEX OF PERSONS

INDEX OF SUBJECTS